THE PAPER AIR FORCE

25 Easy-to-Make, Complete Designs

MICHAEL VOGT

CB
CONTEMPORARY
BOOKS

CHICAGO · NEW YORK

Library of Congress Cataloging-in-Publication Data

Vogt, Michael.
    The paper Air Force : 25 easy-to-make complete designs /
Michael Vogt.
        p.   cm.
   ISBN: 0-8092-4366-0 : $9.95
   1. Paper airplanes.   2. Airplanes, Military—United States—
—Models.   I. Title.
TL778.V63   1989
623.7′46′0228—dc 20   89-22192
                                        CIP

Published by Contemporary Books, Inc.
180 North Michigan Avenue, Chicago, Illinois 60601
Manufactured in the United States of America
International Standard Book Number: 0-8092-4366-0

Published simultaneously in Canada by Beaverbooks, Ltd.
195 Allstate Parkway, Valleywood Business Park
Markham, Ontario L3R 4T8 Canada

I would like to dedicate this book to a couple of teachers up at B.S.U.—
Art and Kerm. They really lived up to what a teacher is supposed to be .
. . they cared when caring counted; they "put out" when "putting out"
really mattered; they took the time to get involved with students'
needs, academic and personal. I think they believed in (and put up with)
some of us even when they were not sure of what we could accomplish.
   This one's for them . . . for believing.

Your friend always,
The "Incredible" Vogt

p.s. Art, Kermie . . . remember these?

"Art" and Kerm" are test pilots. Cut out and place in planes, thrown
from tops of *very* tall buildings, or display with model planes.

Contents

Acknowledgments

I'd like to thank my parents, Chuck and Nancy. They were always there and supported everything we did . . . no matter what.

I'd like to offer a special thanks to the Lord for the gift of a simple and delightful distraction.

Finally, a tribute to my faithful test pilots and flight crew, who mutilated my planes and worked above and beyond the call of duty:

M. E. Vogt, S.B.P.E., Aerospace Engineer
D. M. Gartman, Cadet, Phenomena Class
The Green Bay Headhunter, Cadet, Alpha Class
R. Allen, decd., Pilot, Alpha Class
R. Piorkowski, Cadet, Bozo Class
A. Fracaro, Cadet, Space Class
C. Rosignolo, Cadet, Beta Class
C. Rose, Cadet, Zeta Class
L. Zimba, Cadet, Methusela Class
J. Bogner, Cadet, IDTU Class
B. Koebnick-Vogt, Pilot, Destructo Class
J. W. L. Kentner, Cadet, Bizzaro Class
C. Tome, Cadet, Coach Class
M. TeVogt, Cadet, "Mother" Class
Chuck-the-Bat, Cadet, Rubber Class
P. Vogt, Cadet, Destructo Jr. Class
K. Vogt, Cadet, Silly Class
J. L. Worden, Cadet, Class of '88
B. J. McBob, Mechanic, No Class
E. Earl, Technician, Inviso Class
C. Yeager, Cadet, Mondo Class
E. "E-Man" Kulzer, Cadet, Alota Class

Introduction

The modern paper airplane has been around since the early twentieth century. The basic "schoolboy dart" dates back to when my grandfather was just a kid himself, and it hasn't changed much. (It's time to add a bit of progress.)

An advanced schoolboy dart and many of the planes in this book were inspired by designs shared with me by school friends, parents of school friends, and teachers. I'm sure they were modified and reinvented dozens of times over before they reached me, and I have added many refinements of my own. A scientific/aerospace approach was best suited to this type of development. Computer-aided design and manufacturing methods for design and flight simulation aided the mass construction of numerous variations (over the course of years), testing features, and configurations. These planes were chosen to represent the best-performing craft.

Good luck, and have fun!

chapter 1

Basic Aerodynamics

A paper airplane is just that, a paper *airplane*. So when you begin to construct paper airplanes, you should have a good grasp of some basic principles of aerodynamics, as well as some advanced principles, and how they apply to these paper aircraft.

Almost all aircraft, even helicopters, have one thing in common: a wing of some sort. The wing generates lift through the specially shaped surface's movement through a fluid (air). Accompanying the lift are a corresponding drag and weight of the aircraft. Of course, for the plane to get off the ground, the forward-moving force, or thrust, must be greater than the drag, and the lift generated must be greater than the weight of the aircraft. This lift is caused by a specially shaped cross section of the wing. Here is what happens:

Based on fluid mechanics—the study of the behavior of fluids (water, oils, and gases like air)—the shape that moves through air with the least resistance would look like a stretched teardrop.

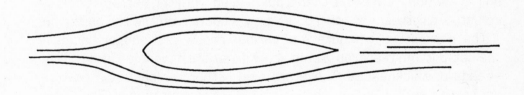

This shape (at low and high speeds) causes the smallest amount of disturbances in the effective "streamlines" of a fluid. Any disturbance a shape causes brings more drag, which should be avoided.

Still, a teardrop shape by itself will generate no more lift than a rectangle, because the flow over the top travels at the same speed as that underneath. But if we were to slice the bottom off, some interesting things would happen.

Now as the section moves through the fluid, the distance the fluid has to travel on top is greater than that on the bottom, so the fluid on top has to move faster, or a vacuum begins to form on the top rear portion of the section. The surface tension of a fluid and the molecular attraction resist this and try to hold together to each other and to the surface of the section, so the fluid speeds up near the top surface, finally catching up to and touching the fluid from beneath the rear of the section. Because of another principle of fluid mechanics, called the Bernoulli effect, when a fluid speeds up, the side force pressure it exerts on a surface drops; hence the pressure from the air on the top drops below that of the bottom and yields a "net" lift.

Note that this lifting force is more accurately viewed as a pulling up on the section from above than a pushing up from the bottom. There is no actual airstream pointing down, only a suction on the top pulling up.

There are literally hundreds of various cross sections, all basically the flat-bottom teardrop. Some show greater efficiencies at different speeds or thicknesses. There are also rather radical sections that generate a net lift, though through slightly different means. These are the ones that usually appear in paper airplanes, so let's consider how they work.

In this supercritical section, the airstream on the top is smooth and nearly flat, but the bottom shows a missing section or "step." When the stream on the bottom encounters this step, it curls in and causes a great deal of *useful* turbulence beneath the wing, actually generating a net lift through an upward pushing force. This force is present for very slow speeds and is enhanced by another force commonly called a lifting body force. The typical "dart" paper airplane has an overall body profile much like this step-discontinuity section that allows the entire fuselage (body) of the plane to generate additional lift.

Besides the basic shape of the section itself, we can add a number of extra things to increase the lift for many of the section profiles. If we simply increase the angle of attack (AOA) of the section—the angle the cord makes with its forward motion—we effectively increase the camber, or curved top surface, and thus speed up the top airflow even more, providing greater lift (and greater drag so the section slows down) to the point of stalling.

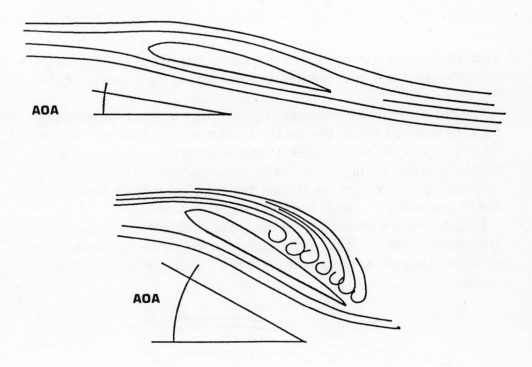

Stalling is a point where the section fails to generate a net lift and is usually accompanied by a loss of control and radical movement caused by the turbulence. During a stall, the airstream on top has to travel too far around the curve and under more pressure than it can withstand, so it pulls away from the wing, causing a severe drop in pressure, almost a pocket. This rapidly fills with air from behind the wing, generating the severe turbulence. Sharp corners on the top of the section camber can also cause this pulling away, because the smooth airstream can only follow a fairly smoothly curving surface and can only stay close to a curve of relatively large radius. As the speed increases, so does this minimum radius of curvature. Because of this, high-speed sections have very little curve (or with some supercritical sections a flattened top), and slower ones have greater curves.

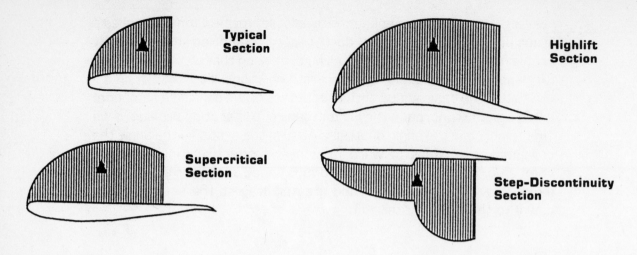

Typical Section

Highlift Section

Supercritical Section

Step-Discontinuity Section

Note: The vertical lines represent the distribution of the lifting force on the cross sections, with the triangles pointing in the direction of the force.

The other mechanical methods of enhancing lift include flaps (on the back, or trailing edge, of the section), slats or slots (at the front, or leading edge, of the section), LERX (leading edge root extensions), wing fences, winglets, and dogteeth. The first three add to the lift of the wing by changing the profile of the section itself; the last three help clean up the lift and make for better flow over the wing itself.

Flaps extend the trailing edge of the section and add to its curvature. They greatly improve lift but at the cost of much increased drag, so are employed typically when slow flight is the object (during takeoff and landing).

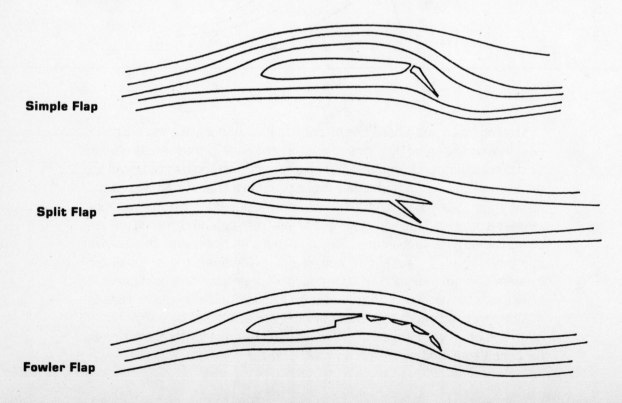

Simple Flap

Split Flap

Fowler Flap

The paper airplanes in this book will typically take advantage of plain or split flaps due to the construction methods used, though you can experiment with Fowlers and any others you can find in good advanced aerodynamics books.

Flaps also exist on leading edges in the form of drooped leading edges or vortex flaps. The drooped leading edge extends the camber and cord of the section much as the trailing edge flaps do, with much the same penalties and benefits. Leading edge vortex flaps are sharp-edged droops that purposely create funnel-shaped turbulence beneath the wing, which adds an extra upward push much like the step-discontinuity section. (These two types of lift are the major working forces in paper planes, more so than actual smooth lift from the Bernoulli effect.)

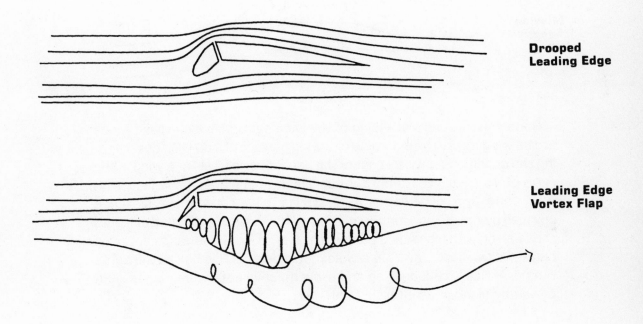

Drooped Leading Edge

Leading Edge Vortex Flap

Slots and slats (movable slots) allow some fraction of air from under the front of the section to flow up and over at a sharper angle to help speed up the air already going over the top. This keeps the airstream on the top from separating too soon and adds to the net lift.

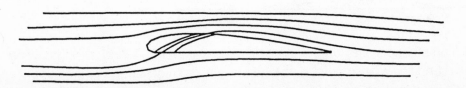

When we combine these high-lift devices, we can really influence the lift generated and produce a section capable of continued flight at very slow and very high speeds. This type of section is generally referred to as "variable camber," or if the curved surface can be kept smooth enough, it approaches what is referred to as mission adaptive wing.

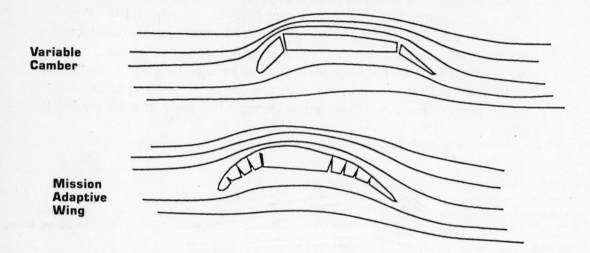

Variable Camber

Mission Adaptive Wing

Based on this understanding of the wing section, we can take a look at the wing itself. The plan view of a wing has a lot to do with determining the conditions it will fly under. The aspect ratio (A.R.) of a wing is the ratio of its length to its cord. Accordingly, sail planes have very high A.R.'s and large glide ratios (G.R.'s). (The glide ratio is the distance covered by a plane horizontally divided by the distance dropped in flight.)

But along with high A.R.'s comes a high drag, so these wings are good only for slow flight. Low A.R.'s yield much lower G.R.'s but at the same time drastically reduce drag and allow much greater speeds, as illustrated by high-speed interceptors.

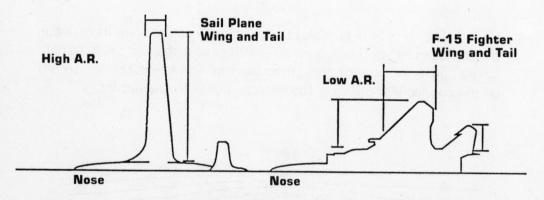

High A.R.

Sail Plane Wing and Tail

Low A.R.

F-15 Fighter Wing and Tail

Nose

Nose

The sweep of the wing is important to its speed. A long, straight wing will tend to twist at the tip at high speeds, so high-speed planes usually sweep the wing back 30 to 45 degrees more to add strength and reduce drag.

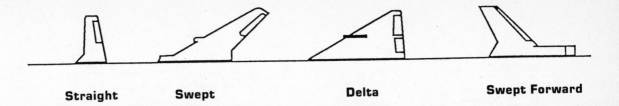

Straight   **Swept**   **Delta**   **Swept Forward**

These swept wings lead to another plan form of the delta wing by filling in the area between the trailing tip and the fuselage (body). Deltas are stable and leave a large amount of room for gear. Between the normal straight, or swept, wing and a full delta is a regular wing with a leading edge root extension (LERX). This is a narrow foil tapering from the wing near the root and extending to the fuselage or all the way along the nose as a chine.

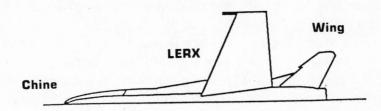

Wing

LERX

Chine

This LERX adds to the lifting surface, sacrificing little additional drag, and smooths out the airstream hitting the wing, leading to a more efficient overall wing performance and an increase in possible angle of attack without stalling.

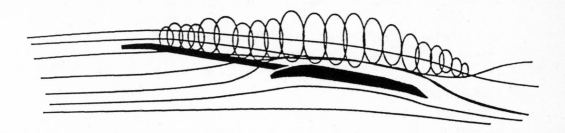

A radical platform that in recent years has become feasible is the swept-forward wing (SFW). Overall it shows the greatest advantages and the fewest disadvantages, but until recently, methods of construction made it impossible to build without making it too heavy. But since our craft are of a scale that can use paper and its rigid qualities, we can build and fly craft that even major aerospace corporations cannot compete with.

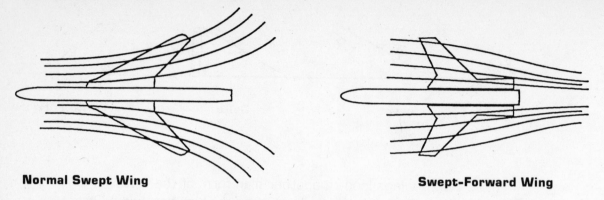

Normal Swept Wing   **Swept-Forward Wing**

The increase in lift with an SFW gives us the option to reduce the wing size and cut weight.

Another important factor in planes, affected by the SFW, is the relative position of the center of lift and the center of gravity. In a normal plane, directional stability is attained by placing the center of gravity ahead of the center of lift. In this configuration, the plane should normally follow a straight path and change only when there is some change in the control surfaces.

In some modern combat aircraft, this is reversed, as in the case of the SFW. Here the center of lift is ahead of the center of gravity, leaving the plane continuously off balance and consistently on the verge of changing its flight path. Only computer-controlled flight systems can keep this kind of plane on a straight path. The benefits that come with this instability are a level of maneuverability never before achieved and limited mostly by pilot conditions. Airplanes like this could easily turn a circle half the diameter of a comparative rear-swept wing plane. Because we cannot yet equip our paper airplanes with digital computers, we will overweight the front and continue to keep the center of gravity ahead of the center of lift.

Following are some plan views of some existing aircraft with their characteristics labeled. Keep in mind that though the next chapter starts with beginner and intermediate craft, in the third chapter we show that we can construct a good flying replica of almost any existing plane.

Plan Views
The following plan views illustrate various working shapes and their strengths.

**Double Delta Wing—
maneuverable, stable at
high speeds**

**Small Delta Wing—
agile at high speeds**

**Broad Straight Wing—
maneuverable, good
weapons platform**

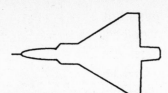

**Delta Wing—
stable at high speeds**

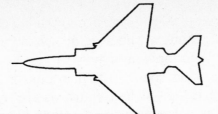

**Large Swept Wing—
good weapons platform**

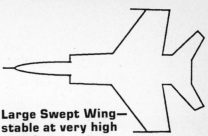

**Large Swept Wing—
stable at very high
speeds**

**Swept Wing with
LERX—agile at high speeds**

**Double Delta Wing
with Canards—large
weapons platform, maneuverable**

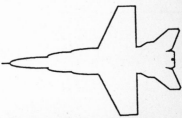

**Straight Wing with LERX—
good weapons platform**

**Double Delta Wing
with LERX—maneuverable,
large weapons platform**

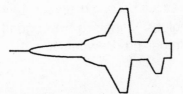

**Short Straight Wing—
light weight, good for
high speeds**

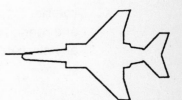

**Short Swept Wing—
agile at high speeds**

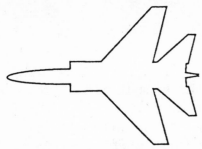

**Large Swept Wing with Canards—
good weapons platform**

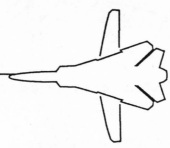

**Variable Swept Wing—
multirole capability**

**Forward-Swept
Wing with Canards—very
maneuverable**

**Very Large, Sharp Delta Wing with Canards—
stable at very high speeds**

A few other devices that don't generate extra lift themselves but that help the overall efficiency of the wing are wing fences, winglets, and the dogtooth. The wing fence is simply that, a strip, sometimes several strips, attached above the wing, to help keep air flowing parallel to the fuselage and keep it from sliding lengthwise over the wing. Only the portion of air that is parallel to the fuselage generates lift; any sliding sideways is just in the way.

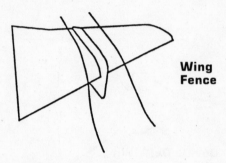

Wing Fence

Winglets are small portions of the wing bent up or down at the tips to prevent spillover on the tips. They perform a function similar to that of fences in that much efficiency is lost from air spilling lengthwise over the tip. This spill also creates strong drag turbulence, which is cut off and made useful by winglets. Winglets are a good addition to almost any aircraft and have almost no drawbacks.

Winglet

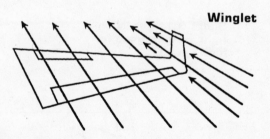

The dogtooth is a notch cut in a wing surface to help generate a constructive vortex that speeds up the air over the top of the wing and eliminate sluggish air that can lower the efficiency of the wing. Cutting a dogtooth in a wing or tail surface can add that extra needed push with very little sacrifice.

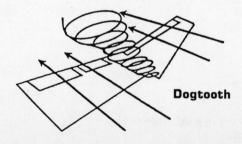

Dogtooth

Control surfaces basically come in two types, vertical and horizontal, though some are combinations of the two. The horizontal surfaces can be located in front of the wing, where they are called canards, or behind the wing, where they are called elevators. Conventionally elevators are used, but this is changing rapidly as the canard gains acceptance. In almost all cases, the canard is more efficient because it continually adds to the net lift of the plane, while the elevator usually subtracts from it.

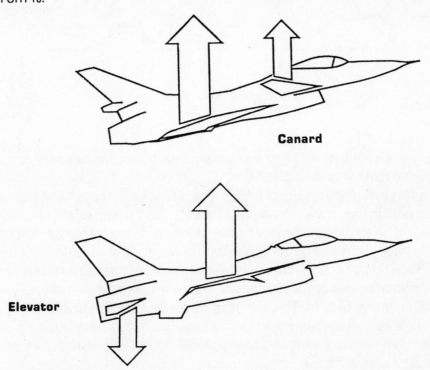

Canard

Elevator

An additional safety feature of a canard shows up as the plane's angle of attack increases. The canard, being in front of the wing, rises first. As the plane approaches its stall angle, the canard will stall before the main wing and lose lift, dropping the nose down again. This makes a canard-based plane nearly stall-proof compared to a definitely unpredictable, stallable, conventional configuration. Still, habits are hard to break, and we will continue to see conventional aircraft produced, as well as delta wings.

For most applications, it is best to keep the horizontal tail surface out of the wake of the main wing. Both are wings and require a smooth, undisturbed airstream in order to work correctly and dependably. Some planes, like deltas, do away with conventional elevators and canards altogether and rely on combination elevator (inboard) and ailerons (outboard) for pitch control (nose up/nose down). This leaves a lot of options, some of which are shown on page 12.

The vertical control surface, or rudder, differs a bit from normal airfoil in that it has a symmetrical section. This is easy to understand because we do not want it to move left or right but to keep the plane on a straight course. The vertical surface has to be big enough to control

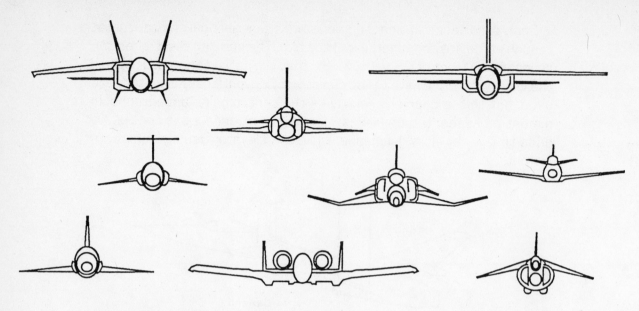

the plane's yaw (left to right movement) without unnecessary drag; otherwise almost anything goes.

One large surface on top is conventional, but twin fins on top yield a better performance at high angles of attack. Some planes also require additional stabilization beneath the plane, but our paper airplanes usually have quite a large vertically flat fuselage, so that is less impor- tant. Twin fins on the bottom are better for most maneuvers but are not feasible for real craft as they are with our paper airplanes. We will take advantage of this. The winglets described earlier are a form of vertical stabilization but are seldom set up as control surfaces.

The relationship of wing and fuselage has a lot to do with the plane's natural stability. This is very important in our uncontrollable paper aircraft. One method typically used on planes to add directional stabil- ity is to set the wing (and horizontal control surfaces) at a *dihedral* angle (with the tips slightly above the roots). To understand this, keep in mind that the useful lift is that portion of the lift perpendicular to the ground, thus opposing the gravity weight of the plane. If a wing is parallel to the ground, all its lift is useful; as the wing rolls, less and less of the lift generated is at an angle useful to counter the weight. When we set the wings at a dihedral angle, as the plane rolls, the wing on the

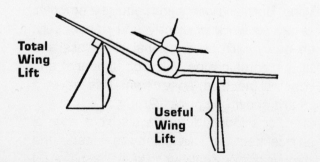

Total Wing Lift

Useful Wing Lift

Extra Lift on One Side

side of the roll generates more useful lift as the wing opposite the roll generates less. This tends to automatically counter the roll and right the plane.

For high- or low-wing planes that are fuselage top-heavy, using a slightly *anhedral* angle (wing tips below the roots) or an inverted gull wing tends to lend stability and prevents rolls by lowering the center of gravity.

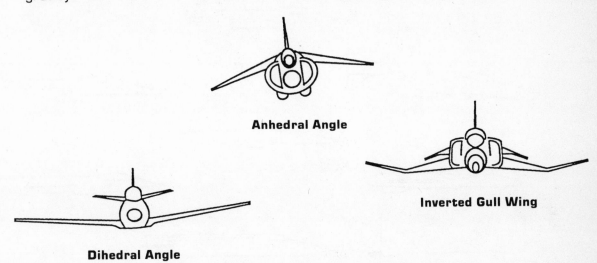

Anhedral Angle

Inverted Gull Wing

Dihedral Angle

Keeping the size of the control surface to a minimum needed to work will require some trial and error but will reward your work with a very efficient design. Some trimming of the tips of surfaces toward the trailing edge will eliminate some unwanted flutter.

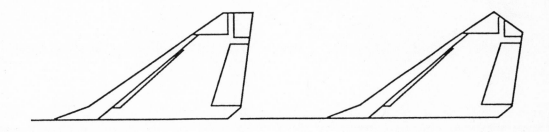

Vertical symmetry from the front is also of *extreme* importance and can be the cause of a great percentage of paper airplane crashes. Care should be taken in all steps of construction to ensure good symmetry, or a winning design will fly like a leaf.

The profiles on page 14 illustrate various combinations of wings and control surfaces.

chapter 2

Beginning and Intermediate Aircraft

Aerobatic Craft

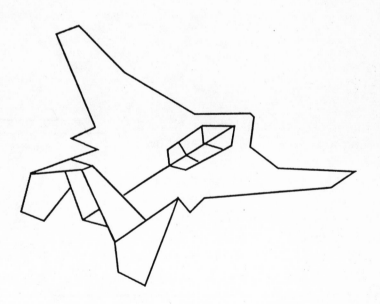

Tight maneuvers usually mean small aircraft with extra strong frames to handle the high g-forces involved. Elaborate control surfaces and exotic wing shapes prevail. In this model, a swept-forward wing and diagonal tail lend extra turning ability.

Start with a small piece of paper. Proportions are more important here than size, though if the paper is longer than 4 inches, it may not be stiff enough. Try 3 × 4 inches first and then different sizes, keeping the length-to-width ratio at about 1⅓-1½. Fold up in half widthwise.

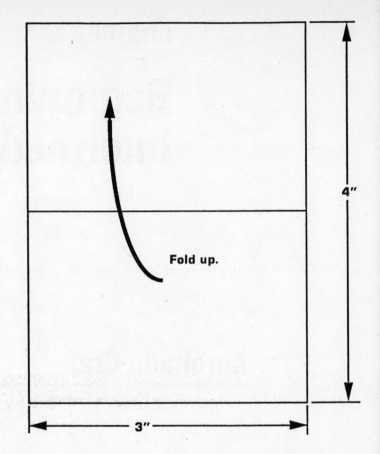

Throughout this chapter, each fold that is the focus of the step is marked by 2 small circles, and accompanied by an arrow showing the direction of the fold. The slashed lines indicate an area to be cut.

Place the paper with the folded side toward you. Sketch the approximate lines, as shown in the illustration.

Make the straight diagonal cut in the top left, cutting through both sides of the paper. Cut out the shaded portion of the leading edge to leave a swept-forward wing. Cut out the top left shaded section, and make the upward small diagonal cut at the bottom right.

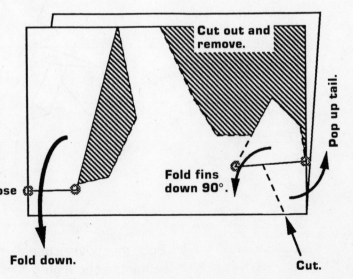

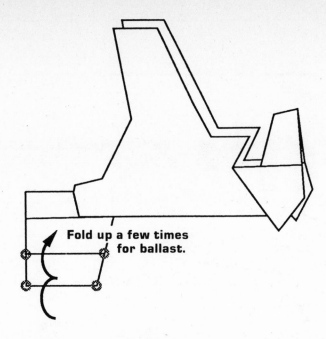

Fold up a few times for ballast.

Fold the small tail fins down, angling a little toward the fuselage. Pop the other little tail piece upward. Press flat.

Fold the top left and right sides separately, one wing and one tail piece at a time, and crease them. Then make several folds up from the bottom till the piece touches the bottom fold of the plane.

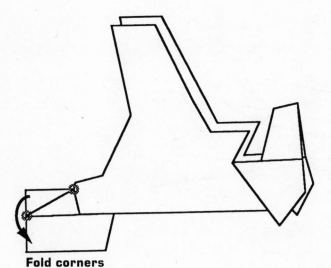

Fold corners down, and tape nose well.

On the little piece in front, fold the top left corner down. Fold the bottom left piece up in half again so it touches the bottom fold of the plane again. Tape this nose weight together.

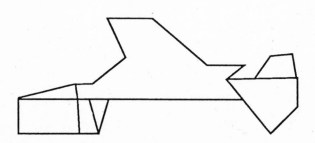

Now spread the wings apart. They should be at about a 135-degree angle to each other. When the plane is viewed from the front, the upward tail piece should form a flattened diamond shape with the wings, and the downward fins should be at right angles to the wings.

This is an easy and very agile little plane. Experiment with many different wing configurations and tail combinations. This plane is fun and unpredictable. (If it could be built life-size, it would make a fantastic pylon racer.)

Interceptors

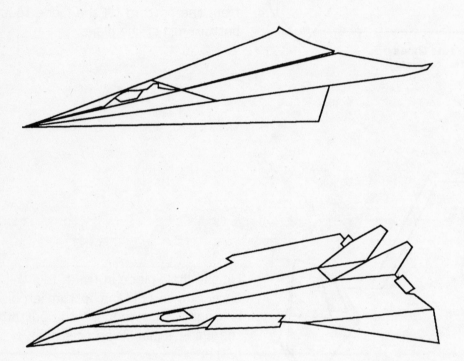

Interceptors must be stable and fast. This variation on the classic dart
has a very swept delta wing to achieve very low drag.

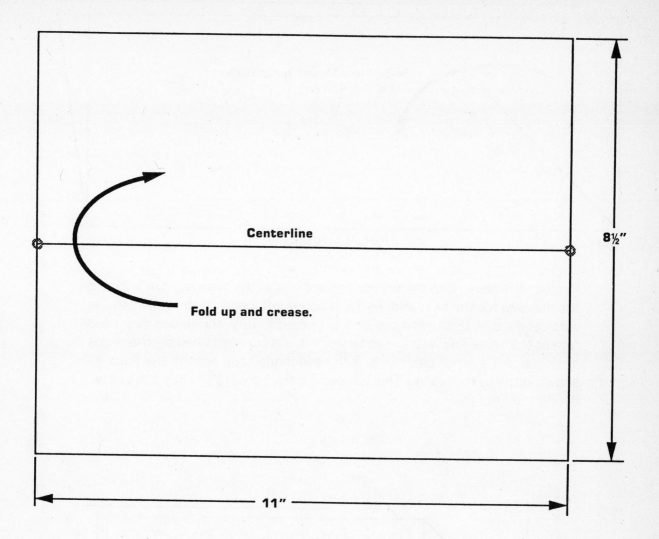

Centerline

Fold up and crease.

8½"

11"

Start with a standard 8½ × 11-inch sheet of paper (the smooth bond paper used in photocopiers was used in this book). Carefully fold it in half lengthwise, matching corners to corners. Gently crease the fold with your thumbnail; flip over and crease again from the other side. Be careful to apply even pressure, and just enough to do the job. It is possible to stretch the fold slightly. Try to avoid this, as it can cause a bow in the length of the plane.

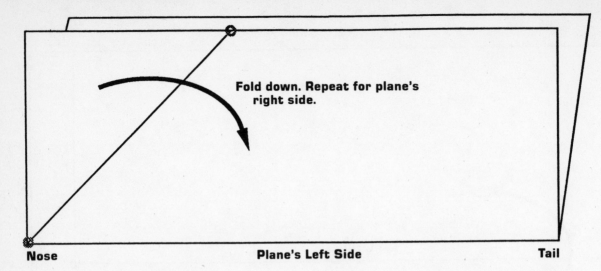

Fold down. Repeat for plane's right side.

Nose   **Plane's Left Side**   **Tail**

Position the paper with the crease toward you. In the drawing at left, locate the position for the next fold. Fold the upper left-hand corner down so the vertical edge is flush with the bottom crease. Turn the paper over, and repeat the same fold with the upper right-hand corner. When both corners are done, put a small piece of ¾-inch cellophane tape across the flaps as shown in the next drawing. This will secure the corners so they don't move during the next fold.

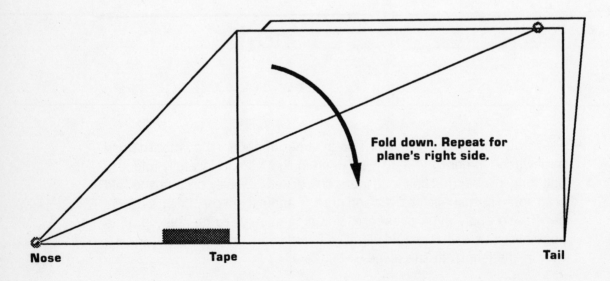

Fold down. Repeat for plane's right side.

Nose   **Tape**   **Tail**

The next fold follows the same direction as the last but runs from the nose point to ½ inch from the rear of the plane. Again, the top left edge will be flush with the bottom when finished. Repeat this fold on the other side, then tape down as before.

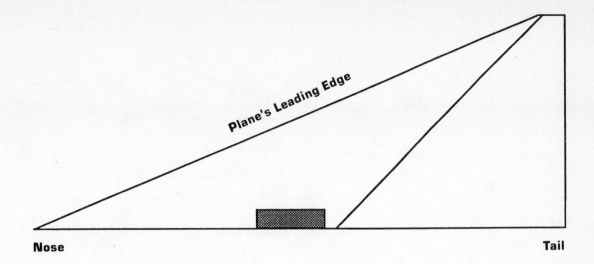

Nose   Tail

The top left-hand edge will be the leading edge. Be sure both wings match. Pay careful attention to these kinds of steps, as they are where most errors occur.

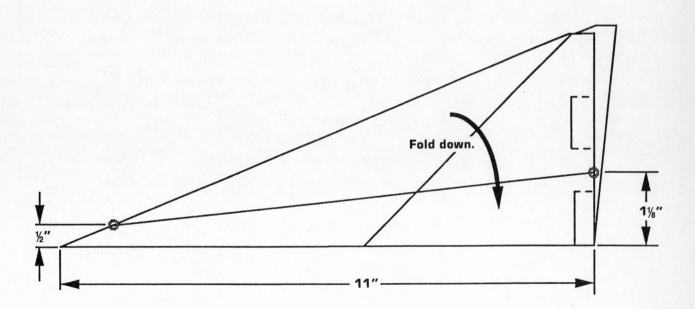

The next fold will go from ½ inch from the bottom on the left to about 1⅛ inches up on the right. You may want to use a straight steel ruler to help you keep this fold straight. Lay the ruler against the paper, and press down on it while you pull the paper up and over it to make the fold. It may take a couple of tries to feel comfortable with this, but it is a technique that will help a lot now and later. Repeat the same fold on the other side of your plane.

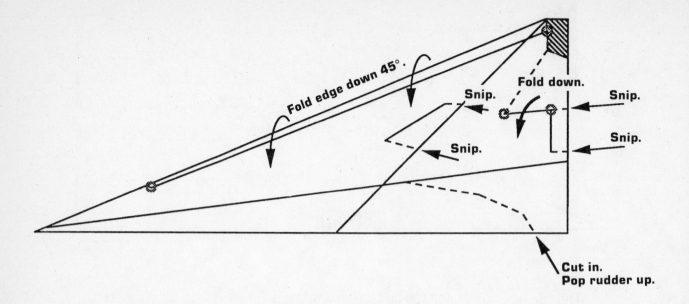

In pencil, lightly mark off the lines shown below. Solid lines are future folds; dashed lines are cuts. In this sketch you can see long vortex flaps, as well as slit flaps, a single dorsal (top side) rudder, two ventral (bottom) fins, and trim tabs on the trailing edge.

Make the cuts and folds you have drawn. Cut through both sides of the plane.

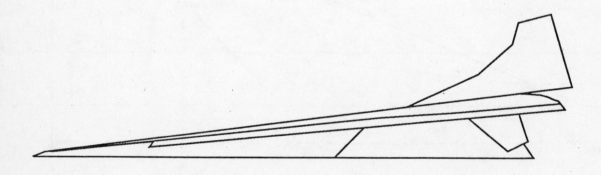

This side view allows you to see the upward position of the main rudder and the downward position of the ventral fins and the leading edge vortex flaps. Review Chapter 1 for the correct position of these flaps.

Note that the wing section is the "step-discontinuity" section.

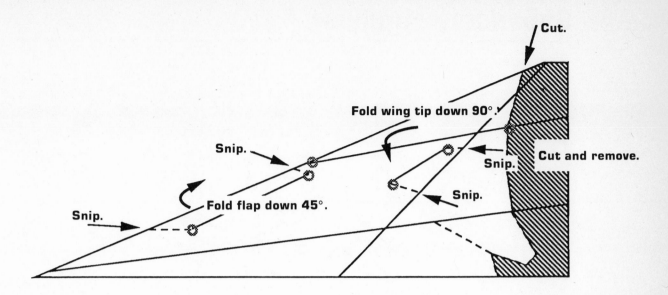

One of many possible variations on the dart is as shown below. It uses normal leading edge flaps but has twin rudders and large, drooped wing tips. The drooped tips should point very nearly down and aid stability at high speeds. The high stability and low aspect ratio make this a good interceptor.

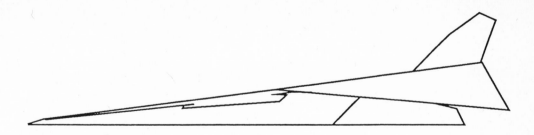

This final profile shows portions of the leading edge flaps and drooped wing tips and twin vertical rudders.

Air Superiority Fighters

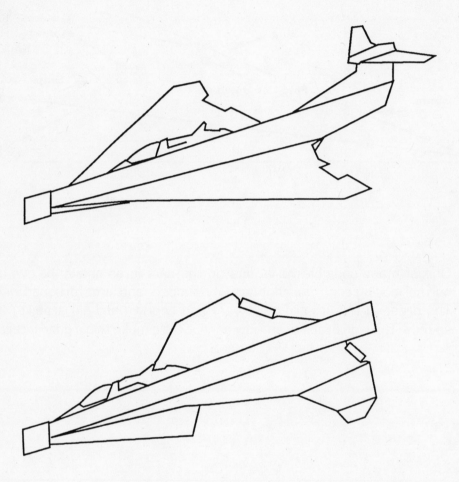

Air superiority fighters rely on low wing loadings and extra control surfaces for much of their maneuvers. Many unique combinations are possible to accomplish this.

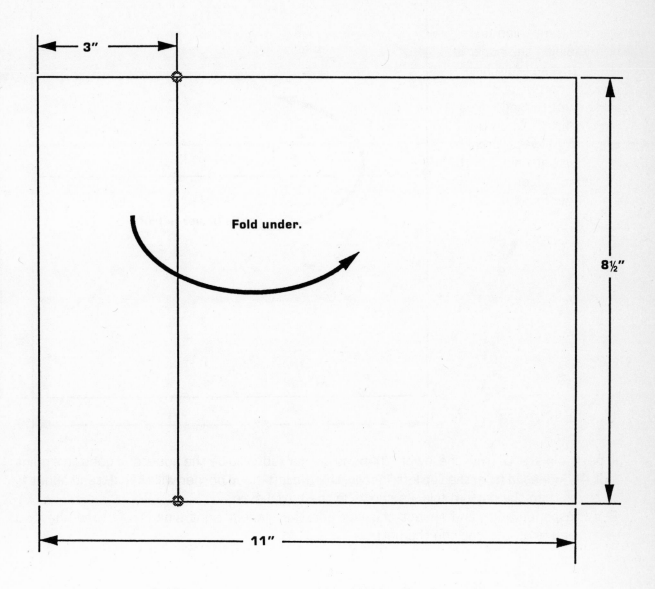

Starting with a sheet of paper approximately 8½ × 11 inches, lightly mark the position for the first fold, which runs along the width, about 3 inches from the left-hand side. Fold along this line. Make sure the top and bottom edges align.

Make the centerline fold next by folding the paper in half lengthwise, matching corner to corner and leaving the exposed edges from the first fold on the outside. As always, crease all folds on both sides with your thumbnail or ruler edge . . . gently.

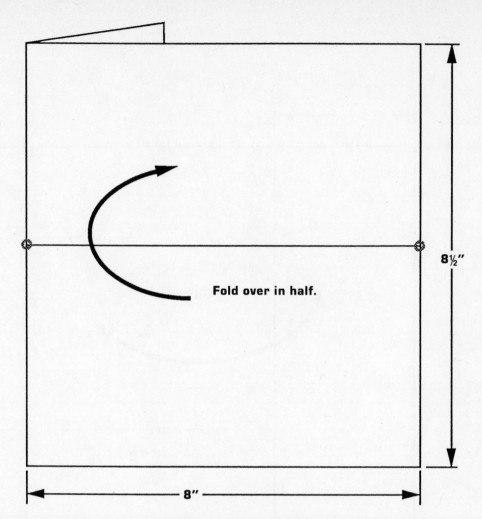

Fold over in half.

8½"

8"

The next fold starts from the lower left-hand corner (soon to be the nose) and goes to a point about 4½ inches in from the top left. Ideally, the top left-hand corner will then extend about ⅝ inch lower than the bottom fold, as shown in the next figure.

Flip the paper over, and repeat this fold for the plane's right side. Then tape the two overhanging ends together on the bottom.

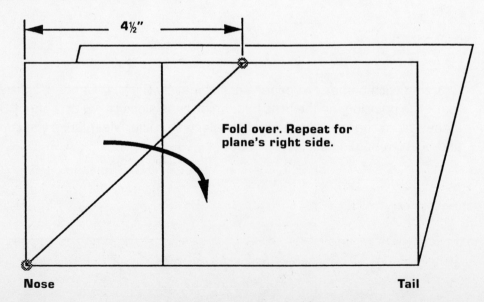

4½"

Fold over. Repeat for plane's right side.

Nose   **Tail**

Choose one of the following two cuts for finishing this plane.

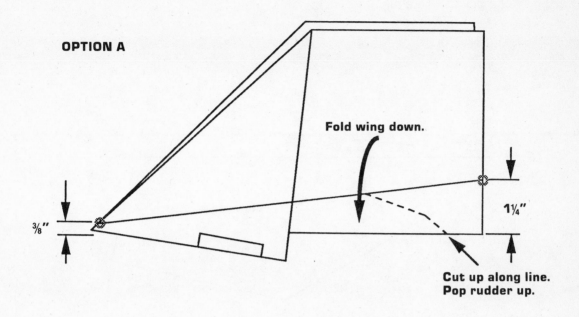

OPTION A

Fold wing down.

$\frac{3}{8}$"

$1\frac{1}{4}$"

Cut up along line.
Pop rudder up.

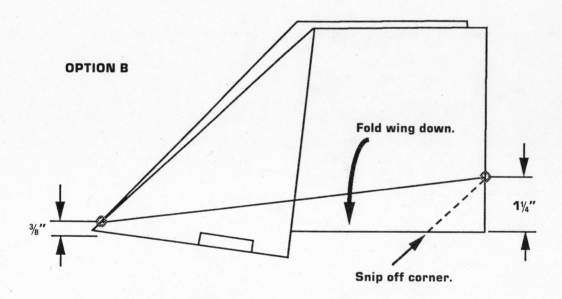

OPTION B

Fold wing down.

$\frac{3}{8}$"

$1\frac{1}{4}$"

Snip off corner.

For both options, the next fold starts about $\frac{3}{8}$ inch up on the left and finishes at a point about $1\frac{1}{4}$ inches up on the right. Fold the wing down, then lay the wing back up, and sketch in the line you chose in Option A or B. Make this cut to the fold.

Fold the left wing back down, then repeat the same fold on the right side of your plane. Secure the bottom of the plane with a piece of cellophane tape.

After folding down the main wing area, lay out the next fold. It starts at the same spot on the left as the last one, but only about ¾ inch down on the right. Mark this fold, then finish it, folding the wing area upward 90 degrees. Repeat for the other wing. Secure the top of the plane with a piece of tape.

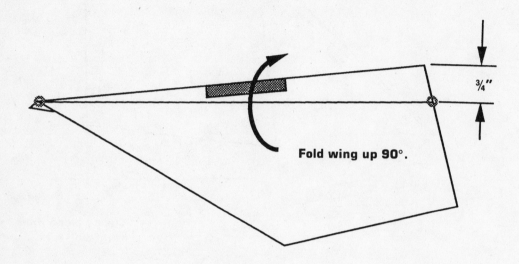

On each wing, mark off the leading and trailing edge areas as shown.

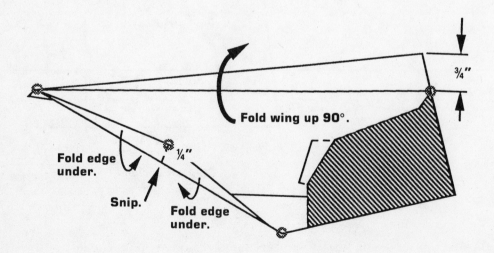

For each leading edge, make a small cut in about ¼ inch, then fold the leading edges under, and tape them down. Cut out the shaded area from both wings.

Option A

If you chose the cut shown as Option A on page 27, continue by using the leftover paper to fashion a T-tail crosspiece. Make a fold down the center of the crosspiece. Pop up the rudder to rise up through the fuselage, and then tape the crosspiece to the top of the rudder.

The T-tail aids in maneuvering by keeping the surface out of the wake of the main wing. This aids the broad main wing in allowing the quick evasive moves that an air superiority fighter is designed to perform.

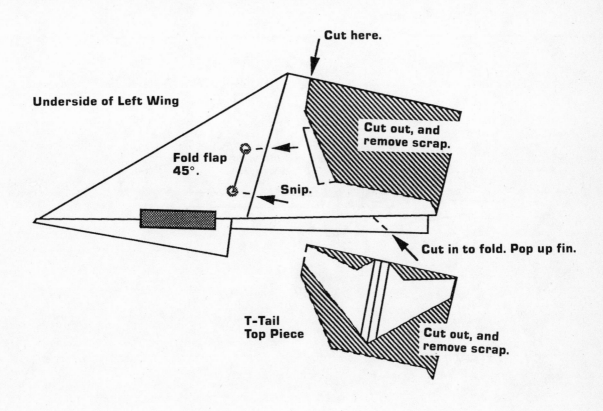

Cut here.

Underside of Left Wing

Fold flap 45°.

Cut out, and remove scrap.

Snip.

Cut in to fold. Pop up fin.

T-Tail Top Piece

Cut out, and remove scrap.

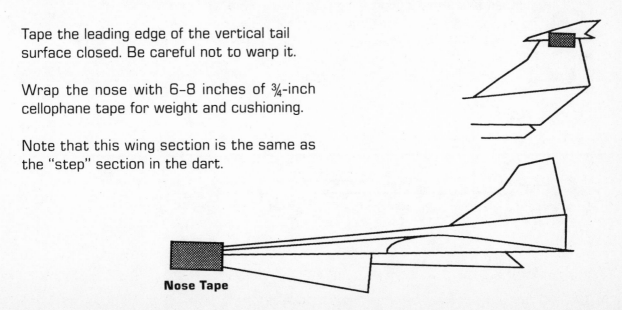

Tape the leading edge of the vertical tail surface closed. Be careful not to warp it.

Wrap the nose with 6–8 inches of ¾-inch cellophane tape for weight and cushioning.

Note that this wing section is the same as the "step" section in the dart.

Nose Tape

Option B

If you chose the cut shown as Option B on page 27, continue by creasing the leading edge well. Fold each wing tip down about 1 inch from the tip.

Wrap the nose with 6–8 inches of ¾-inch cellophane tape. Note that this plane has no vertical rudder, only drooped tips for stability.

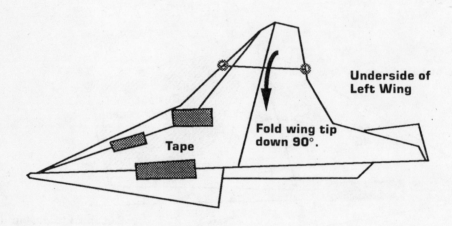

Underside of Left Wing

Fold wing tip down 90°.

Tape

The finished plane has a long cord and broad wing, yielding low wing loading (weight divided by wing area). In air superiority roles, this is important to allow for high maneuverability.

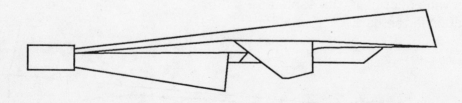

High-Speed Attack Planes

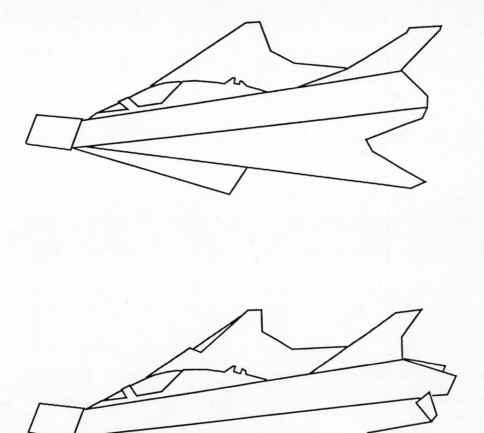

Ideal attack planes have a small, thin wing for reduced drag at low altitudes, and a fuselage large enough to carry abundant ordnances. They must also provide a stable launch platform for these weapons. Pitch control surfaces are of major concern here.

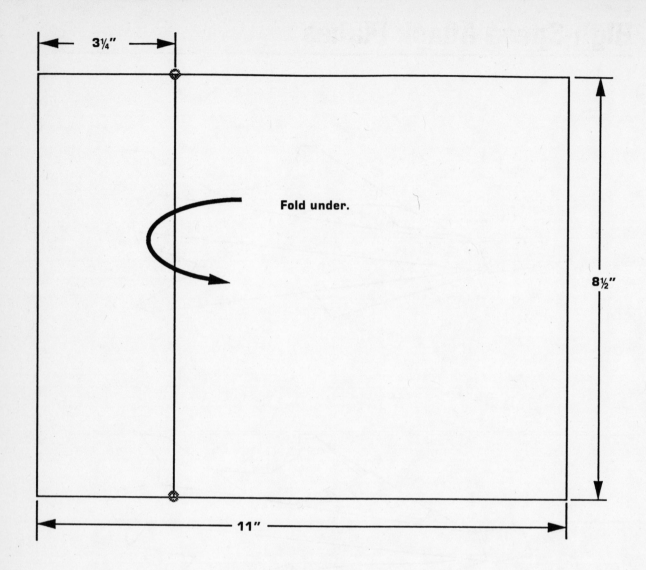

Begin with an 8½ × 11-inch piece of paper. Make the first fold, which lies along the width, about 3¼ inches from the left.

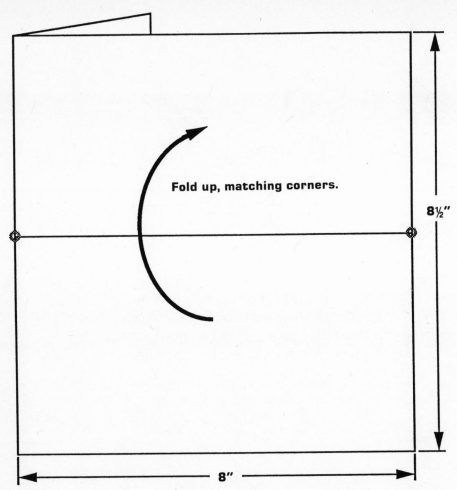

Fold up, matching corners.

8½"

8"

Make the centerline fold second, matching corners and leaving the exposed edge from the first fold on the outside. Then lay the paper with the centerline crease at the bottom (toward you) and the exposed edge to your left.

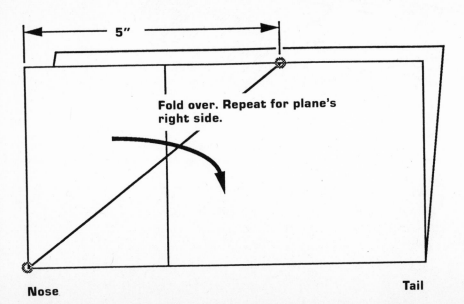

5"

Fold over. Repeat for plane's right side.

Nose

Tail

The next fold starts from the bottom left corner (soon to be the nose) and extends to a point at the top and about 5 inches from the left. Repeat this fold on the right side of the plane. Make sure the leading edges (new top left edge) match. The old top left corners should now extend about ½ inch below the bottom center fold. Tape together the pieces that extend below the center fold.

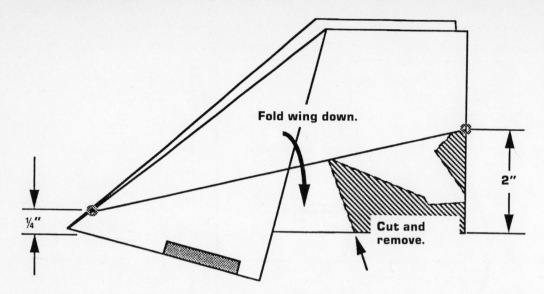

Fold wing down.

2"

¼"

Cut and
remove.

The fold for the major wing area starts at the nose about ¼ inch up from the
bottom left and extends to about 2 inches up from the bottom right. A ruler
or straightedge will help you make this fold. Make the fold on both sides,
then lightly lay out the lines for the future rudder. Cut away the shaded
sections, leaving the tail in place.

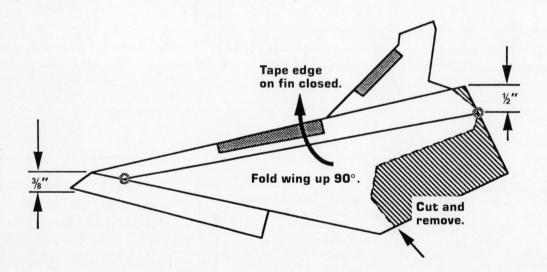

Tape edge
on fin closed.

½"

Fold wing up 90°.

3/8"

Cut and
remove.

With the wing area folded down, lay out the next fold. It will start out about ⅜
inch down from the top left and end about ½ inch down from the top right.
Repeat this fold on the right wing. Tape the top of the fuselage together.

For each wing, cut off the shaded area shown in the outer corner, and snip
off the piece shaded at the back of the fuselage. Pop the rudder up, and tape
the leading edge of the rudder together carefully. It must be straight up and
down and not curve, or it will adversely affect the flight of the plane.

As an option to the last step, cut a large inboard trailing flap and a combination dogtooth-vortex flap leading edge as shown.

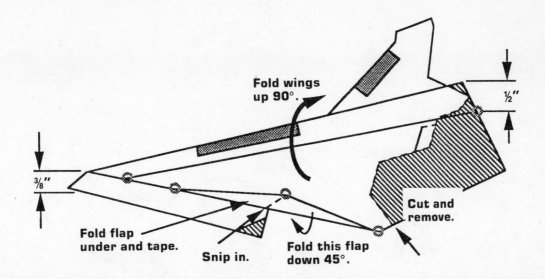

Fold wings up 90°.

½″

3/8″

Cut and remove.

Fold flap under and tape.

Snip in.

Fold this flap down 45°.

For either option, the next step is to cut off the bottom tip of the fuselage and tape it closed. Make the cut into the leading edge toward the rudder. Cut in about ¼ inch. Droop the outboard edge down at about 45 degrees, fold the inboard edge under, and tape it.

Fold each new wing up, and tape the wing root down to the fuselage so the wings stick straight out from side.

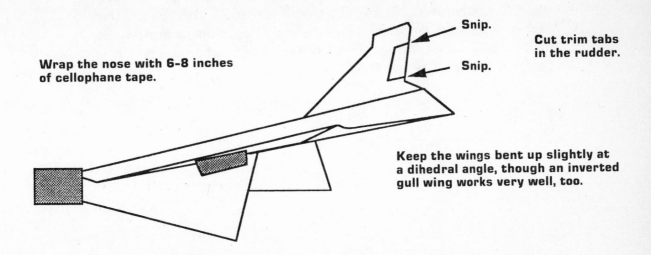

Snip.

Cut trim tabs in the rudder.

Snip.

Wrap the nose with 6-8 inches of cellophane tape.

Keep the wings bent up slightly at a dihedral angle, though an inverted gull wing works very well, too.

The finished plane has a heavy fuselage with short, well-shaped wings to allow for fast, level flight needed for attack roles.

Surveillance Planes

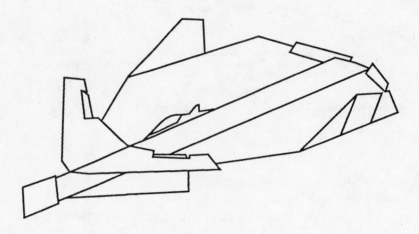

Most reconnaissance (surveillance) planes spend a great portion of their time at high altitudes, where the air is thin. For this reason, they usually have a very large lifting surface area. This takes form in large or multiple wings and control planes. Normal visibility is less important, so cockpits are typically smaller.

Start with an 8½ × 11-inch piece of paper. Make the first fold vertically 3⅛ inches from the left.

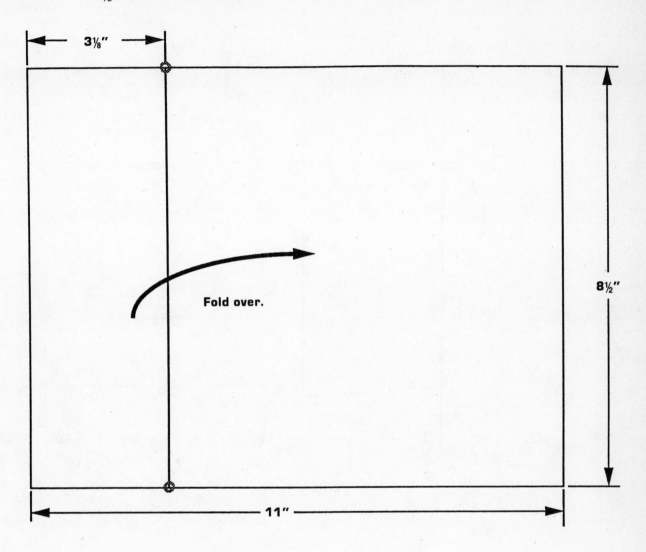

3⅛"

Fold over.

8½"

11"

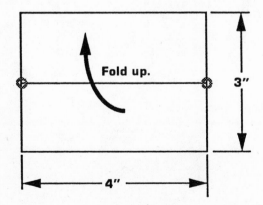

Fold up.

3"

4"

Cut out a separate smaller piece of scrap paper to about 3 × 4 inches, and make a fold down the center lengthwise.

On the large piece, make a fold lengthwise down the center. This time keep the exposed edge from the first fold on the *inside*.

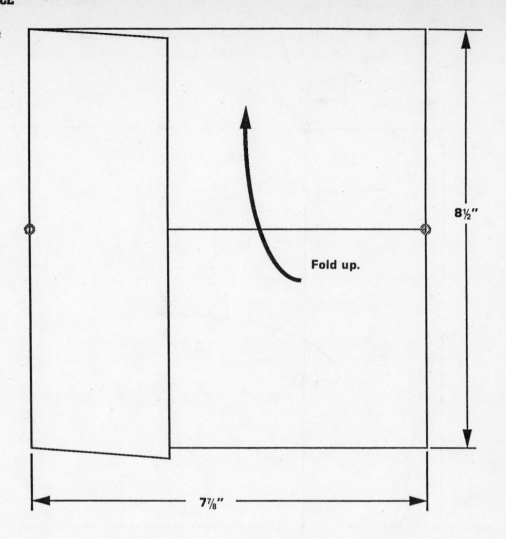

Fold up.

8½"

7⅞"

Fold the smaller piece in half widthwise.

Fold over.

Place the small piece with the vertical fold on the left and the horizontal fold toward you. Cut out the shaded area shown in the drawing. This piece will be the forward canard.

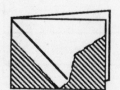

Cut off and remove shaded area.

Fold the canard wings down and to the left along the line in the drawing. There should be only a small part joining the halves, so tape the bottom left side together.

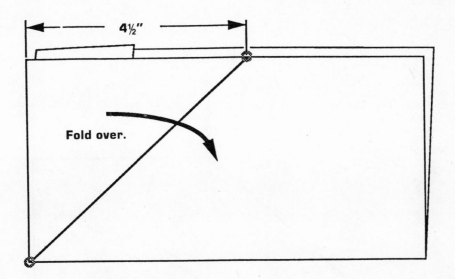

Place the large part with the long fold toward you and the inside fold on the left.

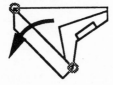

The next fold extends from the bottom left corner to a point about 4½ inches from the left on the top. Repeat this fold on the right side of the plane.

The old top left corners should now extend about ½ inch below the bottom fold. Tape these corners together.

The next fold starts up ⅜ inch from the bottom on the left and extends to a point about 1½ inches up from the bottom on the right. Make this downward fold, then bend back up partway; repeat for the right wing. Lay out the section at the bottom right, and cut out the shaded area. Fold the wing area down again, and tape the top edges together in about the middle.

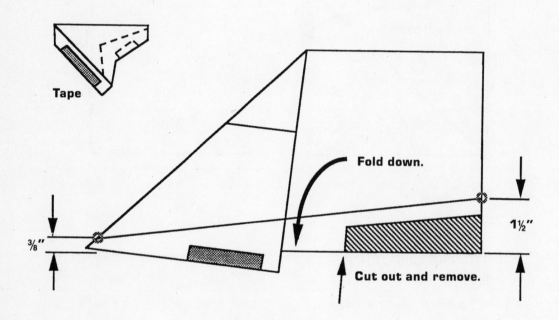

The next fold starts down about ⅜ inch from each end. Lay out this line, and fold each wing up. Tape the new wing root underneath. Lay out the trailing edge lines, and cut away the shaded area. Bend the wing tips upward 90 degrees.

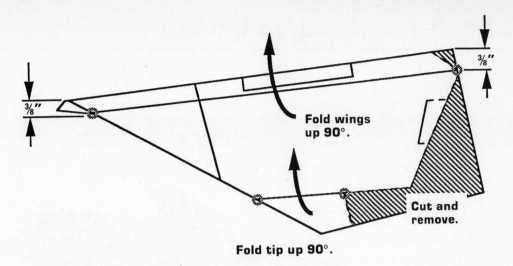

3/8"

3/8"

Fold wings up 90°.

Cut and remove.

Fold tip up 90°.

Insert the bottom left edge of the canard (the edge along which the pieces are taped together) into the top of the fuselage about 1 inch behind the nose. Tape in place.

Wrap the nose with 6–8 inches of tape.

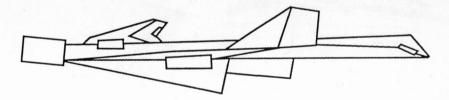

The canard allows for better control and more time aloft. Only a minimum of vertical stabilizer is used, as most of the wing area is used for the lift needed for a high-altitude recon plane.

Advanced-Technology Fighters

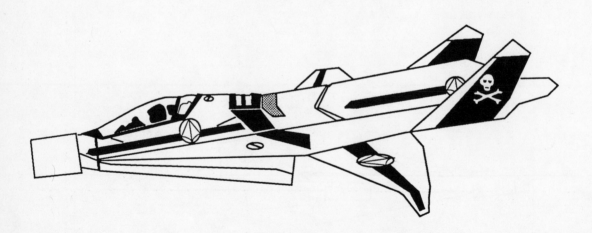

Second-generation fighters employ new lift and control methods to raise performance. New wing planforms (shape of wing from "plan" view, i.e., from above) with multiple cords (cranked arrow) and twin vertical tail fins are proving superior. Variable sweep and camber wings, lifting body surfaces, and winglets are intermediate advances to a completely redesigned aircraft.

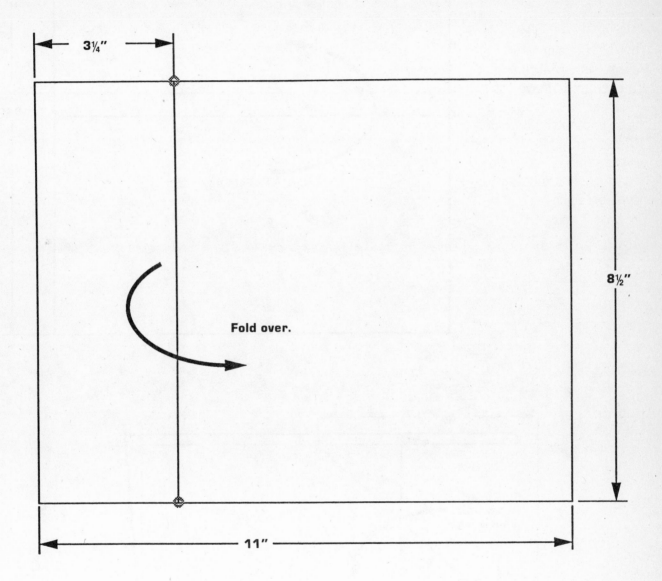

Start with an 8½ × 11-inch sheet of tight, smooth bond paper. The first fold is vertical, about 3¼ inches from the left. After making this fold, lay the paper down with the folded portion underneath and on the left.

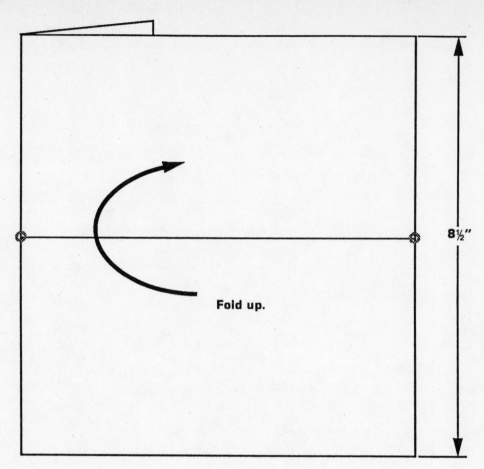

The second fold is horizontal, along the centerline. Match the corners, and leave the exposed edge from the first fold on the outside. Crease well, flip over, and recrease. This will help keep the bottom edge, or keel, straight.

Fold up.

8½"

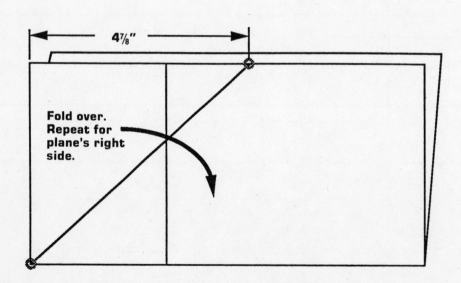

4⅞"

Fold over. Repeat for plane's right side.

With the creased edge toward you and the exposed fold at left, start the next fold at the bottom left corner and extend to a point 4⅞ inches from the left on top. Repeat for the right side of the airplane. The old top left corners will now meet below the center fold. If these tips meet exactly, then the leading edges formed by their folds will match, too. Tape these corners together near the center of the leading edges.

The next wing root fold starts about ½ inch in from the bottom left and extends to the right about ⅞ inch up from the bottom right. Fold down and crease. Repeat for the right wing.

Fold up the wings slightly, and lay out the lines for the shaded section. This strip is 2⅜ inches long and ¼ inch wide. Cut out this section.

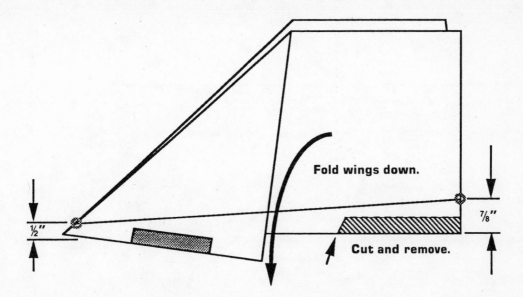

The final wing root fold starts about ½ inch down on the left and ends ⅞ inch down on the right. Fold up each wing, and tape the lower wing root. Secure the top of the fuselage together with a piece of tape.

Cut out the lower right-hand section shaded in the drawing. Make the single straight cut (marked 1) that forms the wing's trailing edge. Slightly to the right of the cut, make the diagonal fold shown. This piece will form 2 sides of a vertical fin. Fold the piece up and to the right (step 2 in the illustration). Tape the root of the fin to the top surface of the wing, then fold the fin up or down for a vertical stabilizer (step 3). Repeat for the plane's other side.

Make 2 small cuts into the leading edge. Fold the 2 pieces under, and tape them down. Crease well.

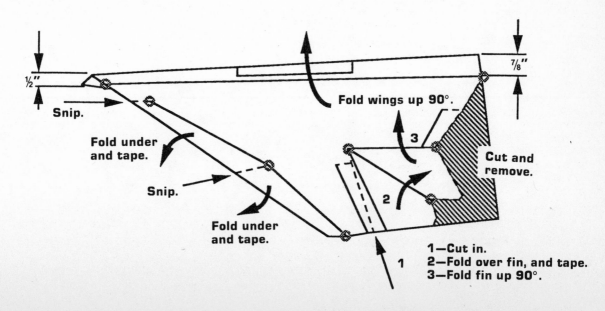

The next drawing shows a slightly different way to finish this plane. Follow the same directions as before, but bend the wing tips down for a winglet, and keep the vertical fins topside.

Note that the fin tips are trimmed to reduce flutter.

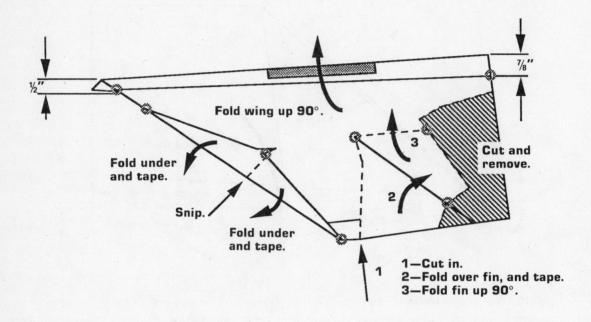

For either option, the final step is to wrap the nose with 6 inches of ¾-inch cellophane tape.

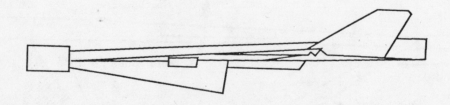

These are the profiles of the first option with upward and downward vertical stabilizers. Because a plane performs more tight moves pulling up rather than down (due to the effect on the pilot), the greater aid to maneuvering would be to place the fins on the bottom. For paper planes, this is fine, as they have no landing gear to be concerned about.

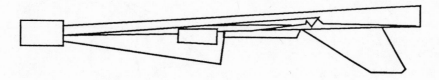

The stiff twin fins on these planes add much to their agility and control. Both have small outer wings with long-cord, broad inner sections. These produce a "lifting body" force and account for the greater part of the entire wing's lift. This wing-body blending is being taken advantage of more and more in second-generation air superiority fighters.

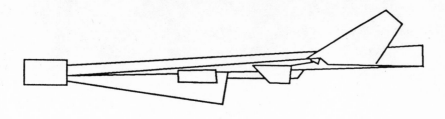

The small keel and winglets make the plane more agile. Maintain a slight dihedral angle.

Flying Wings

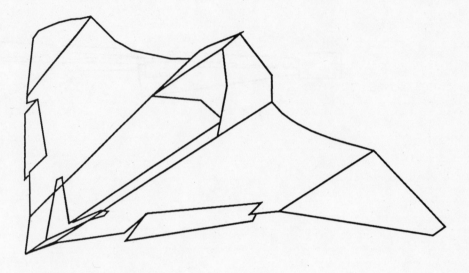

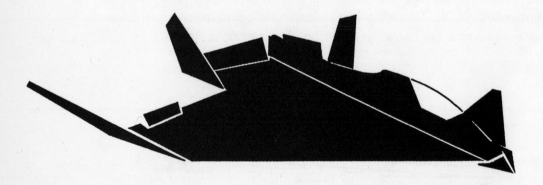

The "flying wing" design has been around for decades. It evolved from the idea that eliminating the fuselage would dramatically reduce drag. The inherent Stealth profile is only now being appreciated. This plane can be constructed from dull black paper to better represent the radar-absorbing coatings that also aid in Stealth concealment.

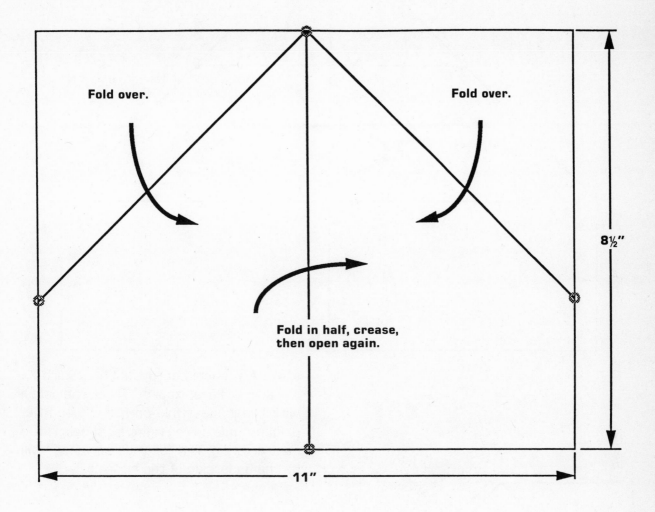

Start with an 8½ × 11-inch sheet of paper. Fold it in half widthwise, crease, and unfold. Turn the paper so that the crease makes a vertical centerline. Then fold the top 2 corners in so the edges and corners meet at the centerline.

Next, fold the new tip down so it meets the point where the 2 corners touch. Crease well.

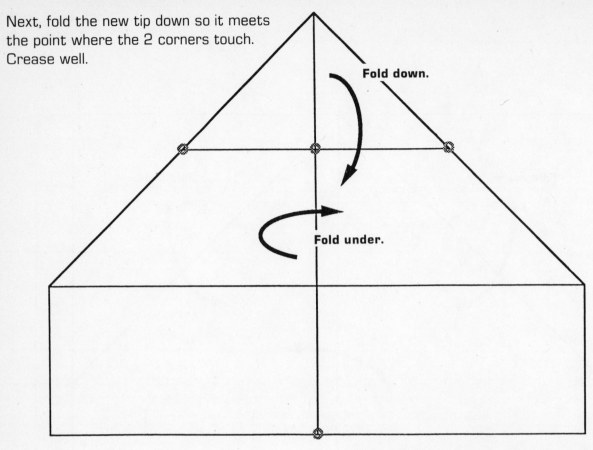

Fold down.

Fold under.

Make a vertical center fold backward so the corners are exposed. Place the paper with the longest fold on the left and the diagonal side on the right, as shown in the next drawing. The "outside surfaces" will be the underside of the aircraft.

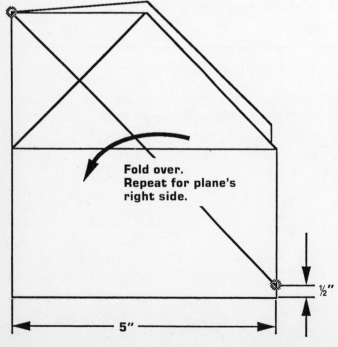

**Fold over.
Repeat for plane's
right side.**

½"

5"

The next fold goes from the top left corner to a point about ½ inch up from the bottom right. Use the top edges as a guide, and fold them so they lie along the vertical centerline. Repeat this fold for the plane's right side. Tape together the corners that now fall on the centerline.

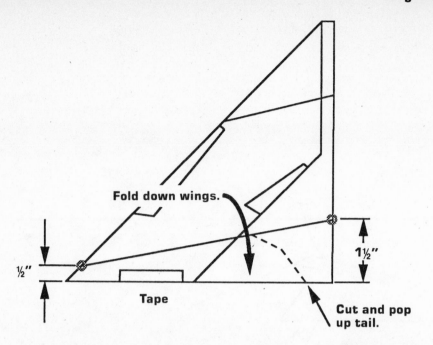

**ALTERNATE TRAILING
EDGE DESIGN**

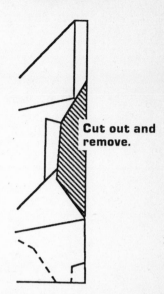

Fold down wings.

½"

Tape

1½"

Cut and pop
up tail.

Cut out and
remove.

Place the paper with the 90-degree angle on the right and the diagonal side at left, as shown in the illustration. The wing root fold starts from the left about ½ inch up from the bottom. It extends to a point about 1½ inches up from the bottom right. About 1½ inches in from the tip of the wing, fold down along a line nearly parallel to the wing root fold. This fold can be at a slight angle outward so the airstream will be deflected outward off the top of the outboard wing. This lends additional stability. Repeat these folds for the right wing.

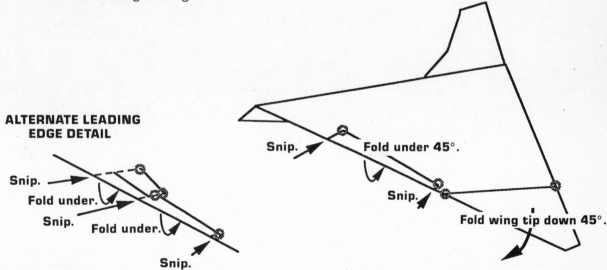

**ALTERNATE LEADING
EDGE DETAIL**

Snip.
Fold under.
Snip.
Fold under.
Snip.

Snip.

Snip front edge flaps free,
then fold down 45°.

Snip.
Fold under 45°.

Snip.

Fold wing tip down 45°.

Side View of Flaps

The inboard leading edge can be cut and equipped with a variety of flaps. Try single and multiple versions. Keep the inboard portions always drooped more than the outer portions. Also try different depths for the cut. Some possibilities are shown in the illustrations at right.

The trailing edge can be cut in several different ways. Making a single cut into the wing root fold will give a vertical rudder that is triangular from the front.

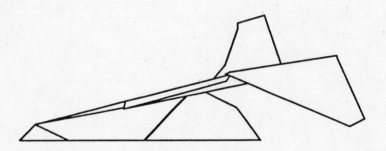

This is a good profile for the flying wing. Folding this plane out of a sheet of black paper makes a good model of the Stealth bomber.

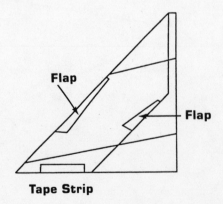

Another variation on the flying wing shows twin tails and a narrower wing cord. When making the initial folds, tape the fuselage on top as well as at the new wing root fold beneath. This plane is a bit faster because it does not open up as much when thrown.

The following illustration shows the steps needed to finish this variation.

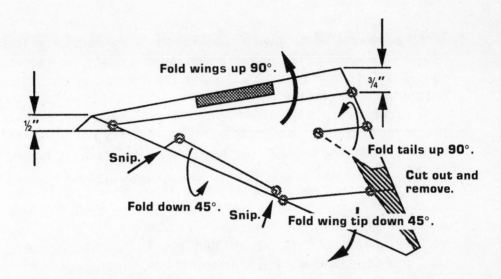

The higher aspect ratio lends the glide ratio that a manned bomber would need. Try this plane with an 11 × 16-inch sheet of paper. It can even be tried with 18 × 26-inch paper to construct a bomber-sized bomber (in the scale of the fighters you have made so far).

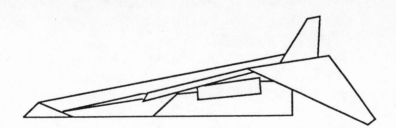

PAPER AIRCRAFT DESIGN AND TROUBLESHOOTING
Tips for Paper Aircraft Design
For the best results and most fun in designing and building your paper aircraft, follow these tips:

- Spend a moment thinking what the airplane is intended for. Is it a high- or low-speed plane? Is it intended for long distance or short, tight maneuvers? These types of questions help decide the shape and specifications for the plane.

- After you have constructed the plane and trimmed and modified it to meet specifications, sacrifice the first plane. Unfold it, trace the folds with a pen, and save it to use as a pattern for future production models.

- Tape loose, exposed edges as you fold the plane. This will ensure nice, symmetrical planes that fly predictably. Quality craftsmanship should be the goal.

- Take the time to make smooth, straight folds. Use a straightedge or ruler, or better yet, clamp the fold under the clip on a clipboard, then pull up on the part to be folded and crease with a fingernail. This works particularly well on long folds.

- When creating a prototype, start a half-dozen models the same way, and only make a minor change in each at the last step. This approach allows you to compare the slight differences to see which optimizes performance.

- Keep a checklist, making notes of features being tested and the flight characteristics of each plane.

- When a plane is finished, give it a preflight check from the front and rear. It is very important that the plane be symmetrical right and left. The wings and control surfaces must match (except possibly the trim tabs). The unbalanced forces caused by asymmetrical surfaces are the major cause for the unpredictable spins and tumbling that untrimmed planes go through.

- Airplanes have cockpits and pilots. Paper airplanes should therefore have paper cockpits and pilots (so says the author).

  Have some fun. Sketch your own cockpits, pilots, ground crew, and soldiers. The ones in this book were drawn about 6 inches high and reduced with a photocopier. Be creative. An advantage of paper airplanes (and figures) is that these can actually be flown and played with, and mass-produced economically. Create an entire air force. Use extras and planes to liven up air combat role-playing games.

  Many things other than planes can fly. Looking at maple trees, one can see where the idea for the Jet Pack pilots came from (that and NASA tech briefs of the sixties).

- Keep planes away from humidity! That is almost certain and irreversible death to a paper plane because the paper absorbs the water and warps. This is why a pattern is so vital. No single plane can last forever, so don't depend on it.

Spraying a good plane with spray acrylic can waterproof it, even make it suitable for a seaplane. This will increase the weight of the plane, so keep that in mind when designing. Remember, a few light coats will not warp the plane and will go on more easily than one heavy coat.

Notes, Specifications, and Performance Keypoints for Paper Airplane Design

Use a note sheet like this (or write directly on the prototype planes) to keep track of changes in the plane's design that are being tested by a particular model.

Keep track of . . .

- the leading edge angles.
- the fore/aft wing root location on the fuselage.
- the wing taper, wing sweep, and the plan view of the wing.
- the cord and span of the wing roots and tips.
- the vertical stabilizer positions and shapes.
- the canopy or cockpit and pilots used.
- the upper/lower keel design.
- the wing profile size, the position of the step in the wing, and the type of cross section used in the wing (i.e., none (flat), normal profile, supercritical, step supercritical).
- the rear horizontal control surface design (i.e., slats, flaps, elevons, elevators, slabs, flaperons, canards, trim tabs).
- the design of the trailing edge.
- the presence of extended wing roots or strakes along the nose.
- the addition of optional new test equipment.

Troubleshooting

Few things work as intended the first time. Here is a short trouble-shooting guide to help you get off to a good start.

Problems	Solutions
Plane noses up repeatedly.	More ballast may be needed in nose. Place extra tape on nose, adjust horizontal control surfaces, and/or move the center of lift forward by adding flaps.
Plane veers right or left.	Check for symmetry from front and rear. Is the vertical fin twisted? Is the fuselage straight? Are the wing pockets the same? Then cut rudder in fin.
Plane tips over sideways or upside down and spirals.	Try altering the center of lift by putting the wings at an anhedral angle or using a gull wing, and adding trailing edge flaps to keep the nose up. Is the cockpit straight?
Plane tumbles into flat spin and crashes.	The center of lift may be in front of the center of gravity. Add ballast to the front. Cut the leading edge of the wing back, fold, and tape under.
Plane's fuselage or nose bends easily and is weak.	Make a "fuselage stiffener" by folding a scrap piece of paper till it is 4 layers thick, about ⅜ inch wide, and a few inches long. Insert into nose and frame, and tape securely. Also try building up the fuselage or nose with tape.
Plane dives to left or right.	Check the position of the horizontal control surfaces. The plane may also require additional vertical control surface area, so add to the fins.
Plane gets damp or wet and warps.	Nearly hopeless. If the warp is confined to a small area, then cut the area out and tape in a new piece. This is why you should make patterns, to avoid certain disaster.

Flight Paths

These are typical flight paths of the interceptor or fighter craft. A bit of rudder trim will add a gentle turn as well.

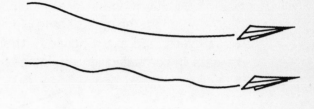

This is the normal path of flying wing or craft with the center of gravity well ahead of the center of lift. You can make most planes follow a dive like this by bending the trim tabs up and releasing the plane gently, not throwing.

Basic aerobatics begin with banks and loops. Bend tabs up, and throw hard at a 45-degree angle to force most planes into a loop. To produce a barrel roll, bend one tab up and the other down.

Adding a bit of rudder trim will not change the initial loop much, but will produce a gentle turn when the extra airspeed bleeds off.

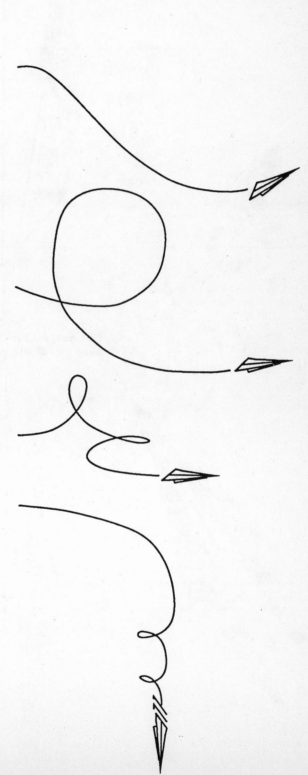

Asymmetrical surfaces and too much ballast will yield this undesirable path . . . straight into the airplane graveyard.

EXTRAS (COCKPITS, ETC.)

The following cockpits and canopies can be taped on or inserted into the previously made aircraft, adding realism to the models. On the following pages are also some playing pieces—little helicopters, Jet Pack flyers, and extra figures—that you can use with the planes as targets in combat-oriented games.

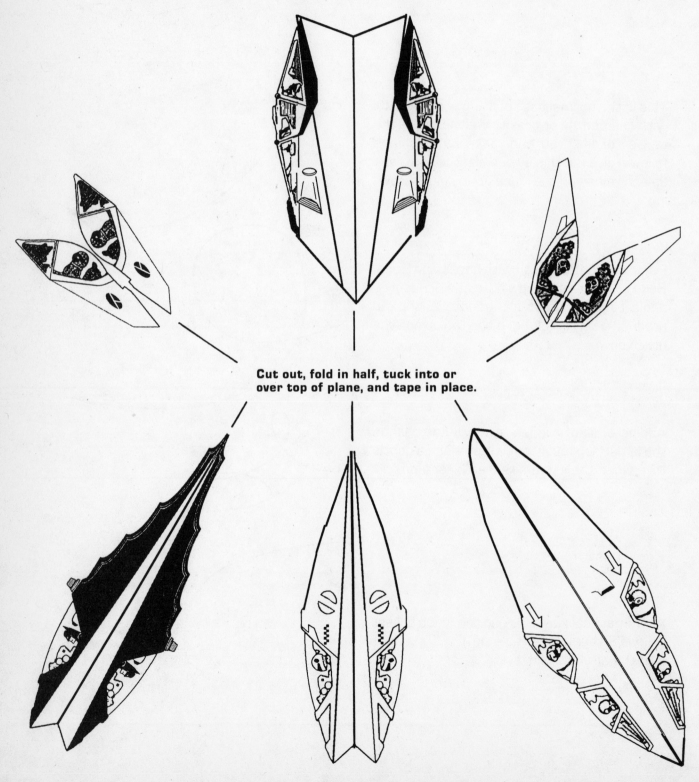

Cut out, fold in half, tuck into or over top of plane, and tape in place.

**Aerobat Cockpit—
Tape on top.**

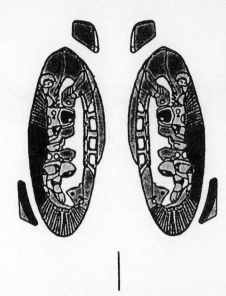

Cockpit for Giant-Size Dart

**Sideview Windows for Dart-Type
Gliders—Tape on sides in front.**

**Flying Wing Cockpits—Tape on
top front of plane. Use a larger
cockpit for 24 × 36-inch paper.**

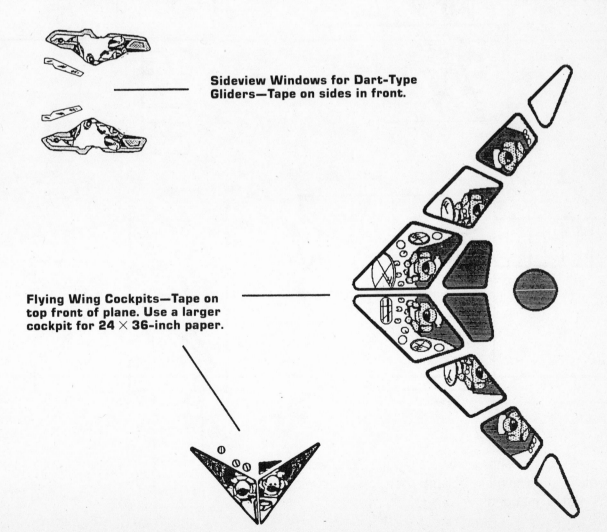

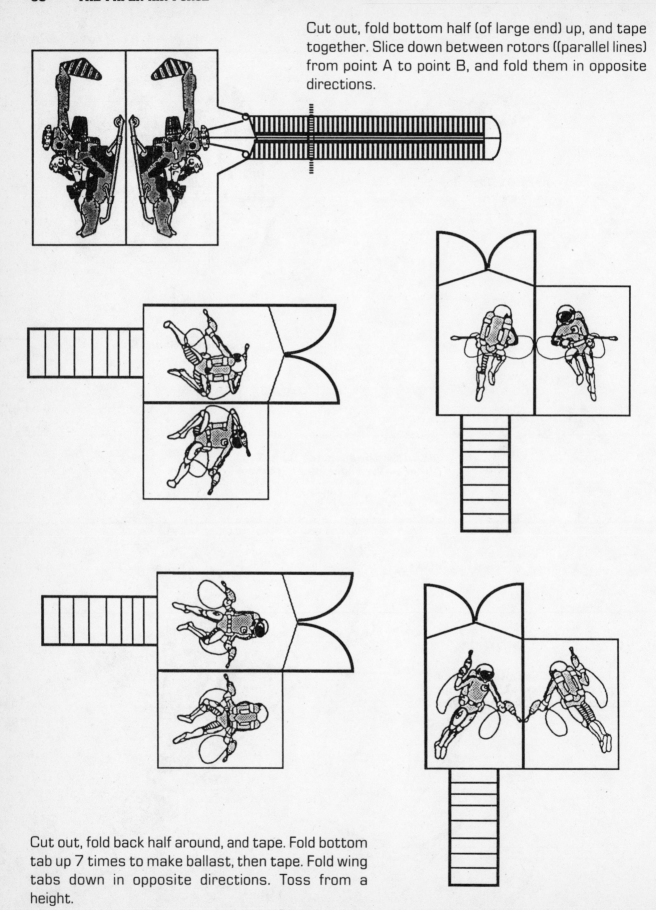

Cut out, fold bottom half (of large end) up, and tape together. Slice down between rotors ((parallel lines) from point A to point B, and fold them in opposite directions.

Cut out, fold back half around, and tape. Fold bottom tab up 7 times to make ballast, then tape. Fold wing tabs down in opposite directions. Toss from a height.

400 Pts DRONE

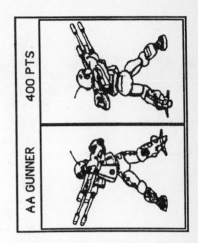

400 PTS   AA GUNNER

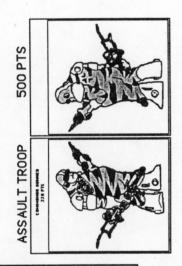

500 PTS   ASSAULT TROOP

600 PTS   POWER LOADER

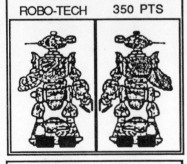

ROBO-TECH   350 PTS

SCOUT   250 PTS

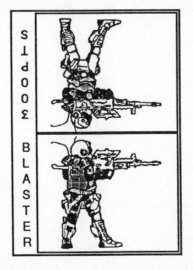

300 Pts BLASTER

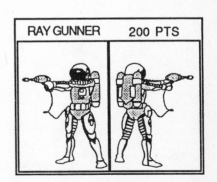

RAY GUNNER   200 PTS

chapter 3

Advanced Aircraft Replicas

Wait until you have folded about a dozen of the beginning and intermediate aircraft (especially the attack planes and advanced fighters) before you move to these advanced craft. These require more attention to detail but follow all the same basic folds and in the same order as used for the intermediate craft. Once you begin a couple, you will recognize that the intermediate air superiority fighter is a very good base from which to develop these advanced replicas.

Some of the main departures from basic craft are the addition of a forward fuselage/nose and sometimes separate taped-on vertical tail surfaces. These are structurally not too important and are mainly for the accurate representation of existing air force aircraft. These planes were even made in scale to each other for added challenge and authenticity.

Some are made heavier than others that are similar, only to show different starting points for your own planes.

A number of the planes require extra stiffening of the fuselage. You can provide this by folding over a scrap piece of paper a couple of times till it is 4–6 layers thick, about ⅜ inch wide, and about 3 inches long. Insert this piece into the fuselage so it protrudes out nearly to the end of the nose. Tape it in place. This adds some weight to the nose, lending much to the plane's directional stability.

The steps involved in all 13 of these planes are almost identical from one to the next, with only a couple of exceptions. A few of the planes have an extra fold at the start to add a bit of weight to the forward area. After that fold, most planes follow the same folds and order as the intermediate air superiority fighter. Refer to it if you have problems. Additionally, the first 3 of the planes' constructions are shown step-by-step. They include 1 plane from each of 3 slightly different styles. Go over them with care, and the other 10 planes will be more familiar.

When making paper airplanes, people tend to rely more on the visual instructions (the diagrams) than on the written. The visual and written instructions are intended to complement each other. In doing so, they may duplicate each other, and sometimes they may be a little different. The intention of the instructions on the folding sheet (the visual) is to aid and remind, but not replace the written instructions. If you use them together, you should have no problem constructing successful aircraft.

Also, please note that for the clarity of these more advanced replicas, the solid lines have been changed to denote cuts, and the dashed lines indicate folds. Familiarize yourself with the information on this page before beginning to assemble the next planes—it will make the projects a lot easier.

Numbers designate folding order.
Colors designate direction of fold.

① — — — — — - **Fold with crease away from you (printing on inside).**

● — — — — — — **Fold with crease toward you (printing on outside).**

✂ ────────────── **Cut along bold lines as required.**
✂ ✂ ✂ ✂

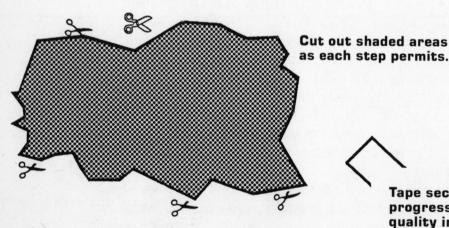

Cut out shaded areas as each step permits.

Tape sections in place as you progress. This will greatly aid quality in construction and yield a sound final product.

Refer to orthographic (side, top, and front) views for any special details such as placement of tail surfaces, noses, and throwing tabs. Also, these drawings show the proper angle at which the wings and tails should be bent.

Follow messages for special operations.

Note: Work only on photocopies! Do not risk originals.

Northrop F-20 Tigershark

Begin by photocopying page 69. Then carefully cut out the 4 major pieces (subsections).

Trim the main fuselage section to the line illustrated. This will make the initial folds easier. The tail and nose sections can be trimmed with less precision for now.

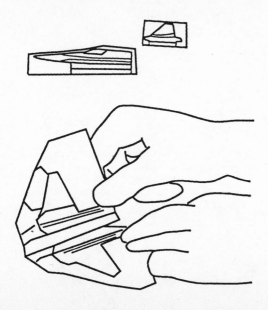

Fold the subsections in half lengthwise along their respective centerlines. Fold the nose with the printing on the outside, but fold the tail and fuselage with the printing on the inside. Holding the pieces up to a light will aid in lining up the left and right sides. Crease the folds well.

On the fuselage, fold each side down along the line numbered 2 so the printed fuselage shows but not the white inside of the fuselage. When viewed from the end, the fuselage should look like the letter *M*.

Trim the tail and nose sections closely. Then fold the nose sides down and then back up again, ending with an accordian-shaped stiffener built into the nose.

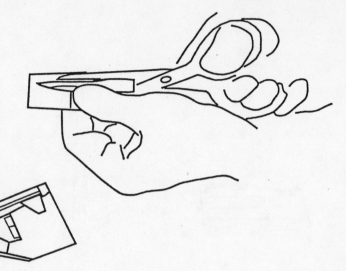

Trim the shaded (diagonally striped) areas away from the fuselage. This will leave the wing and tail surfaces and a flap on the leading edge of the wings.

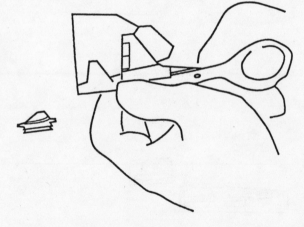

With the under-wing pieces folded and taped, there should be 3 complete subsections waiting to be joined.

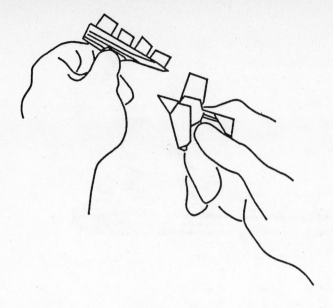

Tape the nose piece into a stiff, flat panel, using a number of small pieces of tape. Tape the bottom of the fuselage together, and prepare to slide the nose over the front of the fuselage. You may have to slice back some of the tape to allow a good fit of nose to fuselage. Keep a razor handy for this.

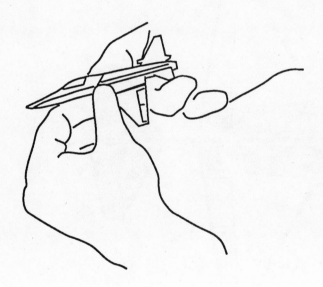

Slide the nose over the outside front of the fuselage so the inside folds match. Some slicing along the folds may be necessary. Take some time to adjust these two parts so the stripe lines up as shown in the final illustration. Tape the nose securely in place.

Next slide the tail in place, and tape it securely.

Bend the wings and tail up to a slight dihedral angle, and cut the small trim tabs marked on the tail.

Fold under the flap on the leading edge of each wing. Tape the flaps down to strengthen the wing. Tape together the shaded portions to form a thumb-hold on the bottom for ease of throwing.

The finished product is fast and maneuverable. Try coloring in the gray. The original craft wore bright red with a white stripe.

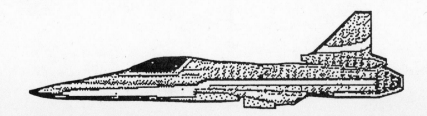

Orthographic (Side and Front) Views

These drawings are designed to aid in placement of parts during construction. Note that they are the same size as the actual models.

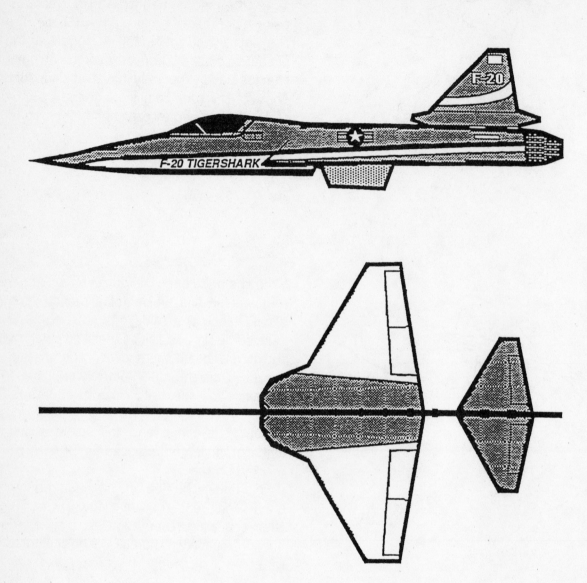

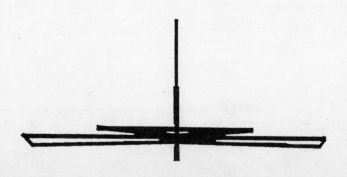

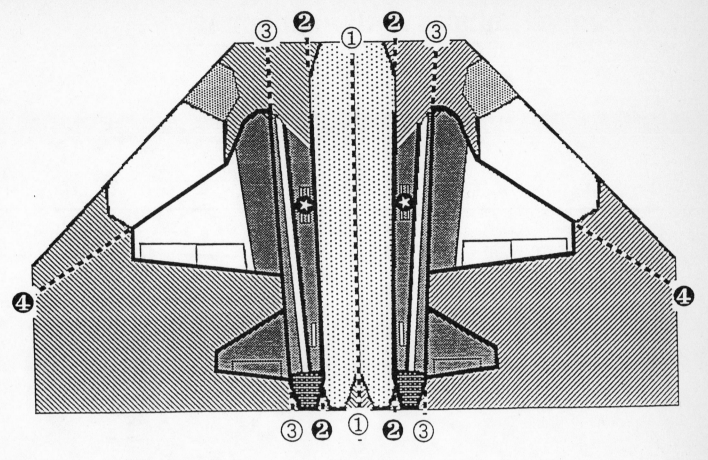

Fuselage

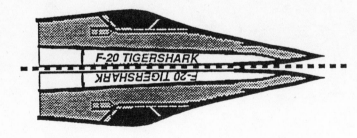

Cut, fold, and tape over forward fuselage.
Tape well for ballast.

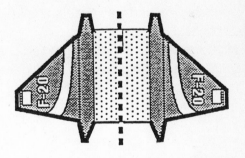

Cut, fold, tape, and insert
into rear fuselage.

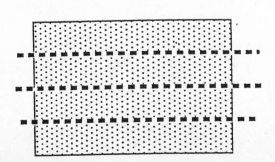

Fuselage Stiffener—Insert inside
forward fuselage between nose
and main section.

McDonnell Douglas F-4E Phantom II

Photocopy page 77 or page 79. (The plane on page 79 is an alternative version of the plane on page 77. The markings are different, but the instructions are the same.) Cut out the 4 main pieces: nose, cockpit, tail stiffener, and main fuselage. Trim the fuselage close, as shown in the illustration.

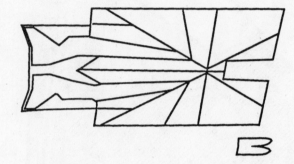

Fold the cockpit, nose, and tail stiffener in half lengthwise, and trim to follow lines. Tape them together.

   Fold each white leading edge piece under, following the line numbered 2. Crease. Be sure to watch that centerlines match.

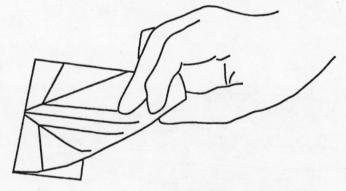

Fold the fuselage in half lengthwise along the centerline, matching corner to corner. The printed design will be on the inside.

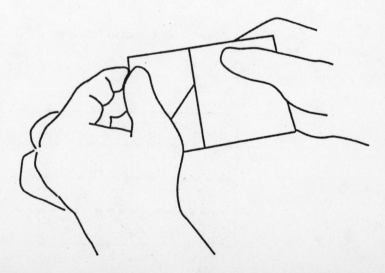

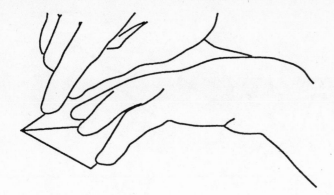

Crease the centerline well (remember the straightedge ruler technique).

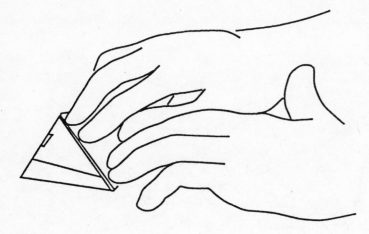

Fold down one corner, carefully following the diagonal line numbered 4 on the wing. Crease well.

Fold down the second corner along the corresponding diagonal line to match the first corner. It is more important for the corners to match than for the diagonal lines to meet exactly. The symmetry of the plane lies more in the alignment of the corners and paper than in the illustrated detail.

Tape the corners together along the bottom of the plane. Note that this is very similar to the advanced-technology fighter in Chapter 2.

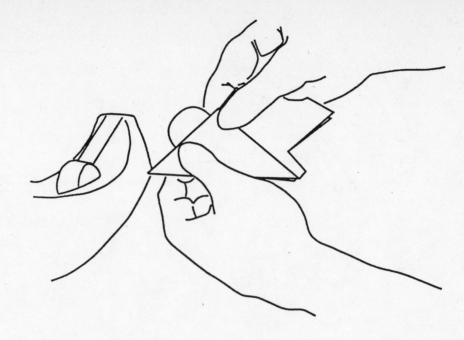

Now trim the tail surfaces at the rear of the fuselage. Most of the line detail is on the inside, so it will help to hold the piece up against a light to see the cutting lines through the paper.

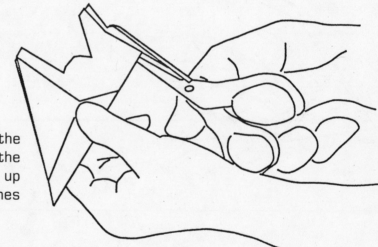

With the tail surfaces cut out, prepare to fold the wings down (actually up in the picture).

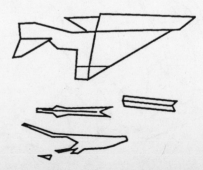

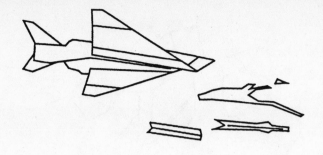

Fold the first wing down along the heavy black line numbered 5. Try to expose as little white area from the inside of the fuselage as possible.

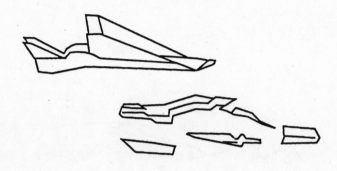

Fold the second wing so the leading edges match. Let the tail turn itself right side out. Try not to put creases in the tail surface.

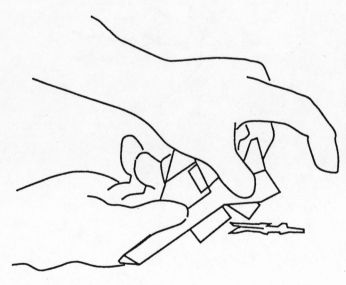

Tape the leading edge of the tail closed and the top of the fuselage shut. Tape close to the back of the fuselage, as the cockpit will be slid into the fuselage toward the front. Be careful not to twist the tail while taping it. If you do, slice the tape, and try again. A warped tail will greatly upset the plane's stability.

Locate the heavy black line joining the left wing to the fuselage. Fold the wing back up toward the top of the fuselage. Repeat for the other wing, matching leading edges again. Fold the tail surfaces up along their lines.

Tape the underside of the wings to the fuse-lage at their connection. Crease the fold well. Tape the back of the tail together. From the rear view, the tail should look like an inverted Y.

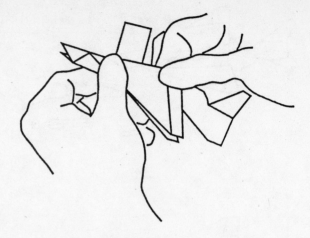

Locate the lines on top of the wings about ⅓ of the way from the tips. Bend up these tips slightly, and crease them. Then bend them down again so they form about a 160-degree angle with the inboard part of each wing.

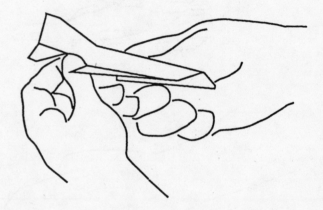

Trim the fuselage stiffener, and insert it in-side the rear lower fuselage so the black diamond-shaped area fits into the corner below the tail surfaces. Tape across the stif-fener as it is inserted. This will keep the tail from bending too easily side to side.

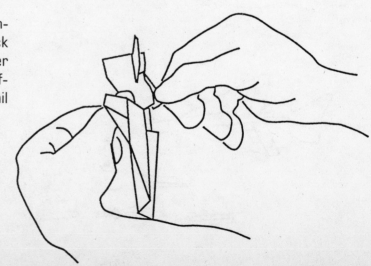

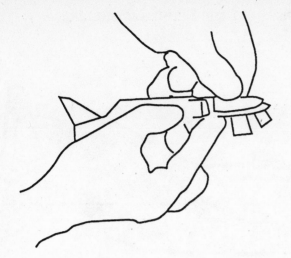

Trim the nose section, and slide it over the front of the fuselage. Follow the drawings on page 76 to aid in placement of nose section. The flat part of the top of the fuselage and that on the top of the nose should form one straight line with no angles. This will leave the nose drooping slightly.

Tape the nose section in place, and add extra tape to the nose to reinforce it.

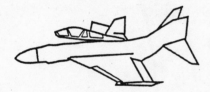

Trim cockpit, tape it together, and insert it into the upper forward fuselage so the cockpit just touches the rear of the nose piece. Tape it in place.

Cut the rear flaps marked on the trailing edge of the wings, and begin your preflight inspection.

The final product represents the best combination of detail and performance.

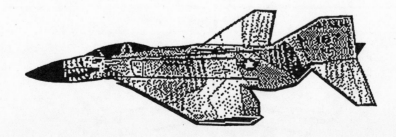

Orthographic Views to Aid in Placement of Parts During Construction

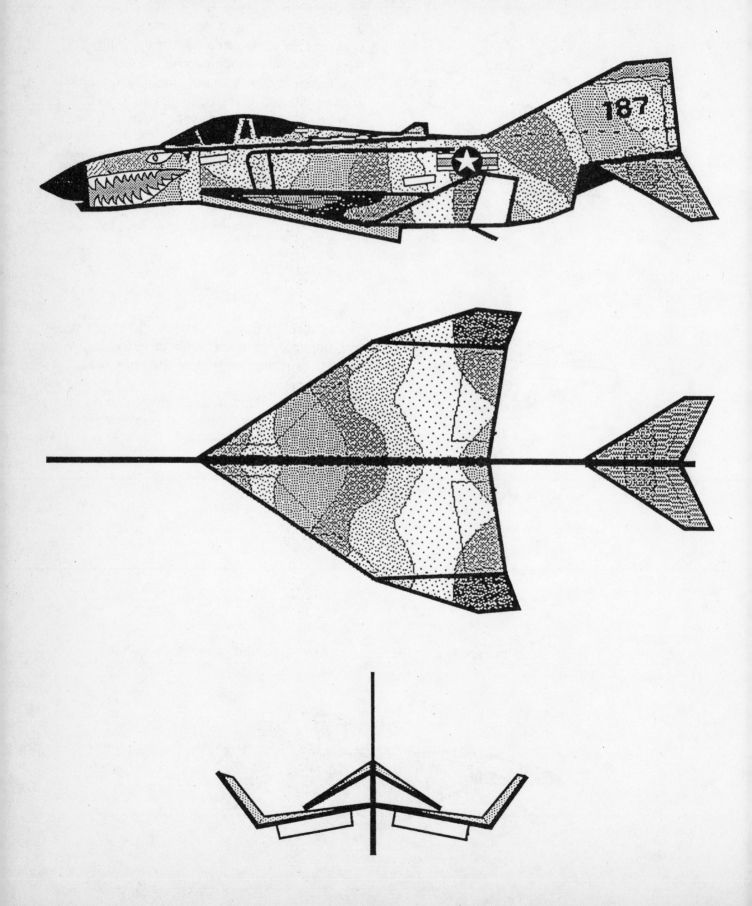

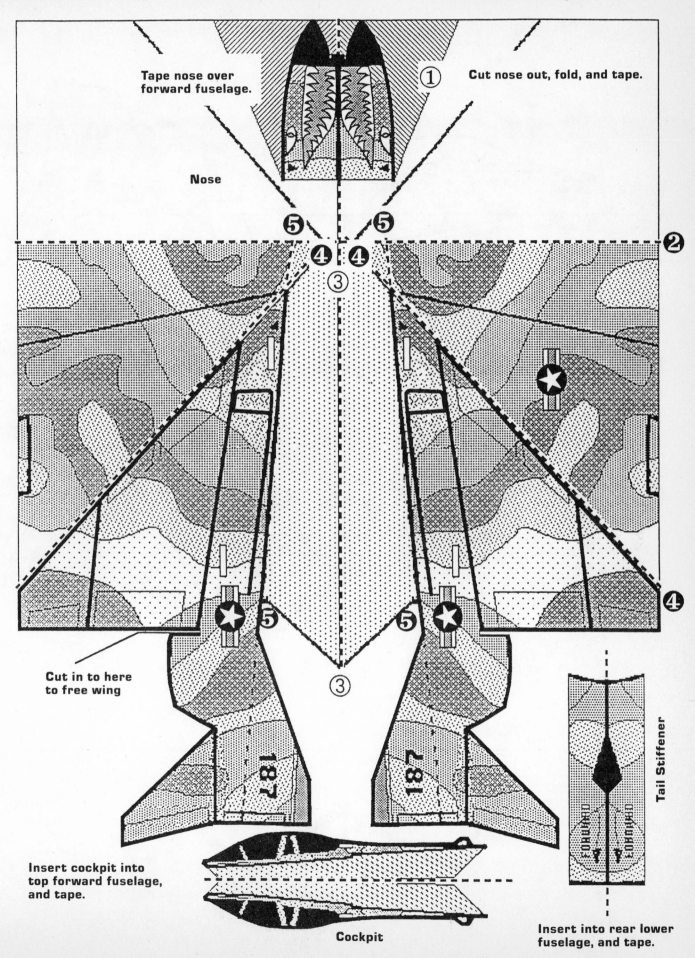

Tape nose over
forward fuselage.

① Cut nose out, fold, and tape.

Nose

⑤ ⑤

②

④ ④

③

★

★ ★ 4

⑤ ⑤

187 187

Cut in to here
to free wing

③

Tail Stiffener

Insert cockpit into
top forward fuselage,
and tape.

Cockpit

Insert into rear lower
fuselage, and tape.

Orthographic Views to Aid in Placement of Parts During Construction

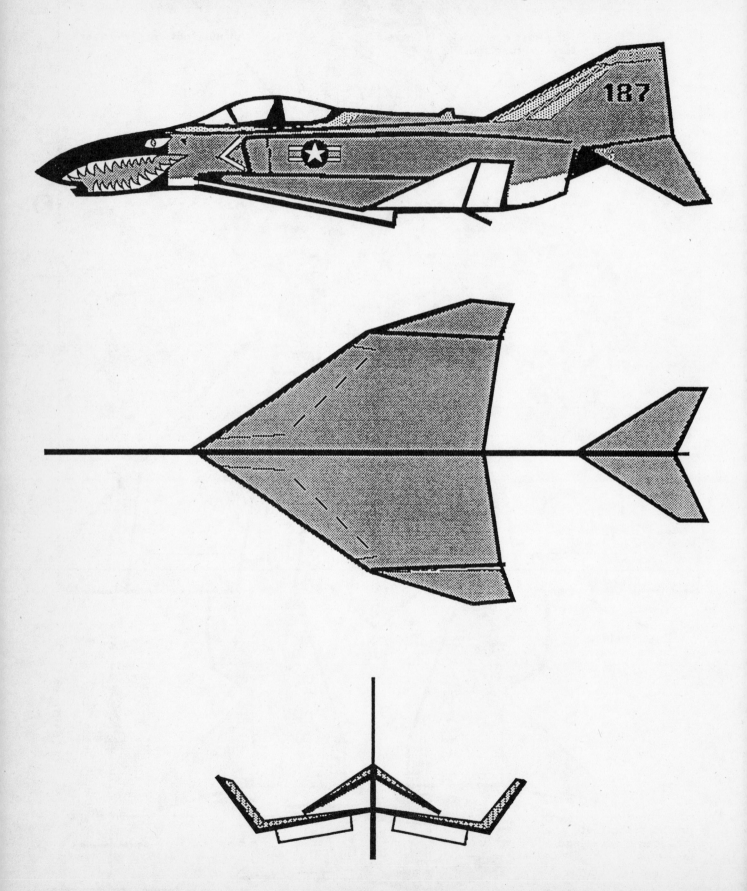

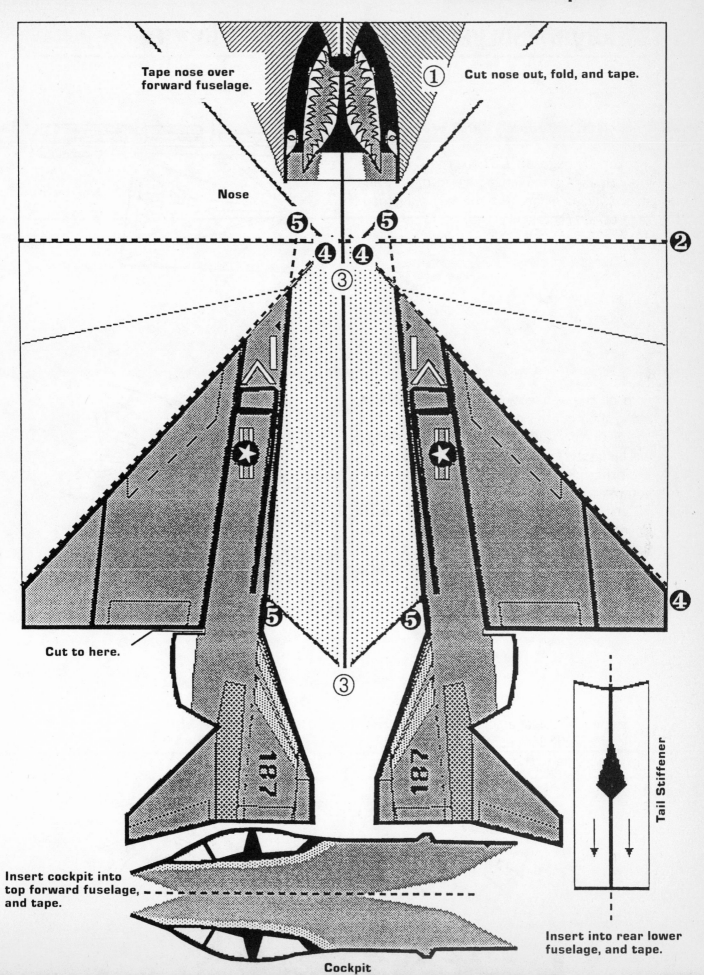

Tape nose over forward fuselage.

① Cut nose out, fold, and tape.

Nose

⑤   ⑤

②

④ ④

③

⑤   ⑤

④

③

Cut to here.

Tail Stiffener

187   187

Insert cockpit into top forward fuselage, and tape.

Insert into rear lower fuselage, and tape.

Cockpit

Mikoyan-Guryevich MiG-23/27 "Flogger"

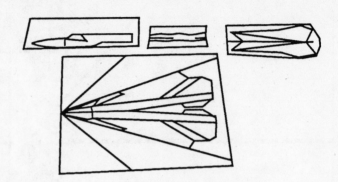

Photocopy page 85. Cut out the 4 subsections: nose, tail, midfuselage stiffener, and main wing fuselage. Trim the main wing fuselage to the rectangular line.

Fold all the subsections in half lengthwise along their centerlines as shown. Note that the design printed on the main wing fuselage will be on the inside, whereas the designs on the other pieces will be on the outside after you make these folds.

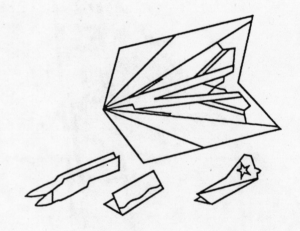

On the main section, be sure to match corners to corners so the centerline will be correct. Hold the small subsections up to the light to aid in aligning the sides during folding. Trim the sections to shape.

On the main fuselage, fold down one corner along one of the lines numbered 2. Repeat for the other side of the plane. Tape down each corner.

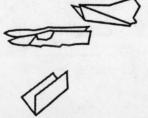

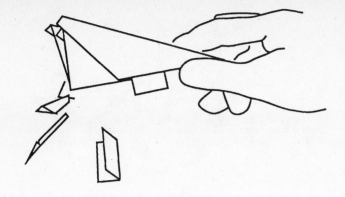

Make the second fold down for each wing along the line numbered 3. Tape the lower corners together at the bottom of the fuselage.

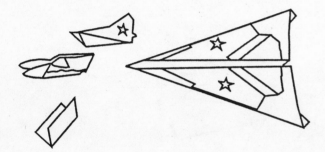

Fold each wing down a third time—along the lines numbered 4—exposing the final shape of the wings. Try to let the white inner fuselage be the guide for folding. Crease well.

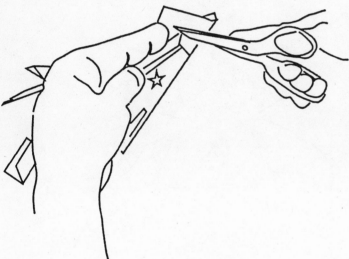

Trim the shaded (diagonally striped) area away from the rear of the fuselage and around the wing tips. Leave the white area between the wing and tail surfaces on both sides.

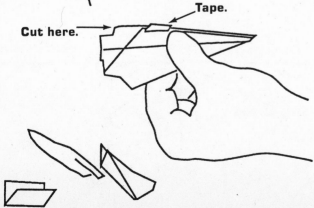

Make a cut in the lower rear of the fuselage as shown, to expose the lower rear fin (the white segment drawn near the rear of the plane). Hold the plane to the light, and use the heavy solid lines as a guide.

Snip the nose off the fuselage along the heavy line. Make a small cut into the leading edge of each wing at the illustrated dog-tooth. These cuts are located at the side of the white area on the leading edge of each wing.

Fold down the white inboard leading edge piece on each wing, and crease. Tape each piece under.

Fold the wings back down, insert the nose piece into the fuselage, and tape it in place. Leave the top open for additional stiffener if needed after the plane is completed.
Tape up the nose section with a number of small pieces of tape to reinforce the nose and seal the seams.

Insert the tail into the upper rear fuselage, and tape it in place. Tape the leading edge of the tail fin closed. Be sure to keep the fin straight and vertical. Take your time, and do a good job. Refer to the orthographic drawings on page 84 for correct positioning.

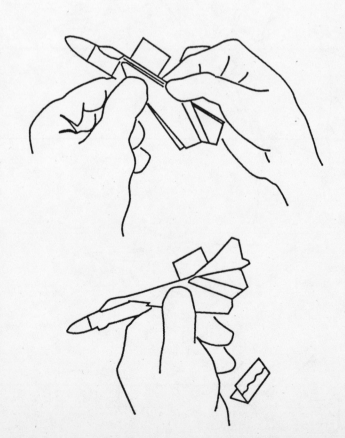

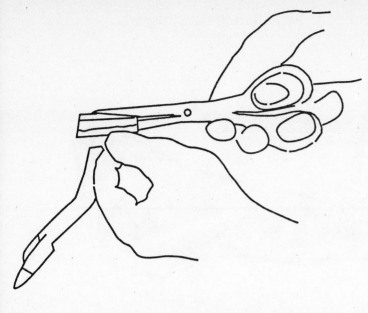

The stiffener should just tuck up under the wing. Trim it to blend in and fit snugly. Tape it in place.

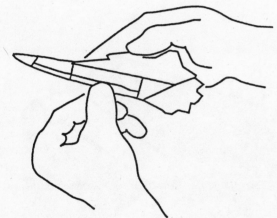

The final subsection is an additional stiffener. Trim it so it completes the bottom edge between the lower nose and the lower rear fuselage.

Here is the final product. Add tape as necessary, and bend the wings down to a noticeable anhedral angle. This angle shifts the center of weight and adds stability.

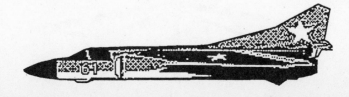

Orthographic Views to Aid in Placement of Parts During Construction

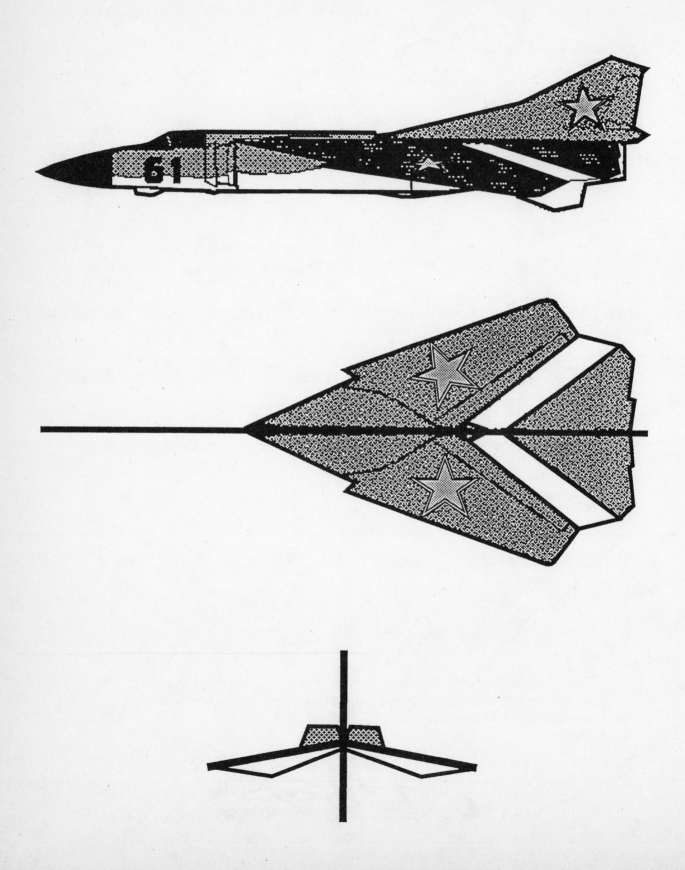

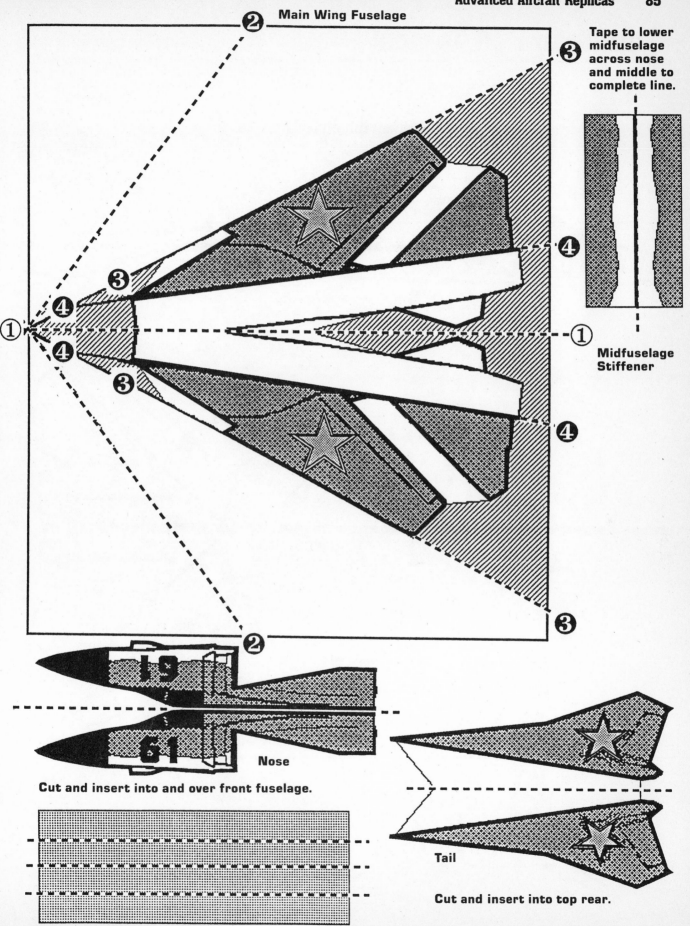

② Main Wing Fuselage

③ Tape to lower midfuselage across nose and middle to complete line.

Midfuselage Stiffener

Nose

Cut and insert into and over front fuselage.

Tail

Cut and insert into top rear.

Fuselage Stiffener—Insert between nose and front.

Grumman F-14 Tomcat

Orthographic Views

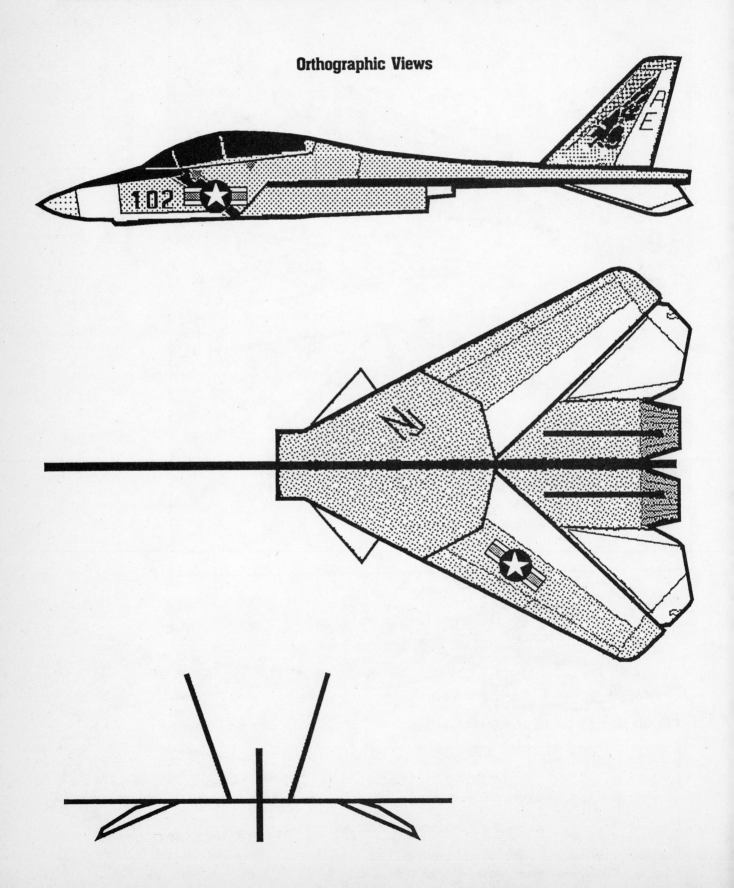

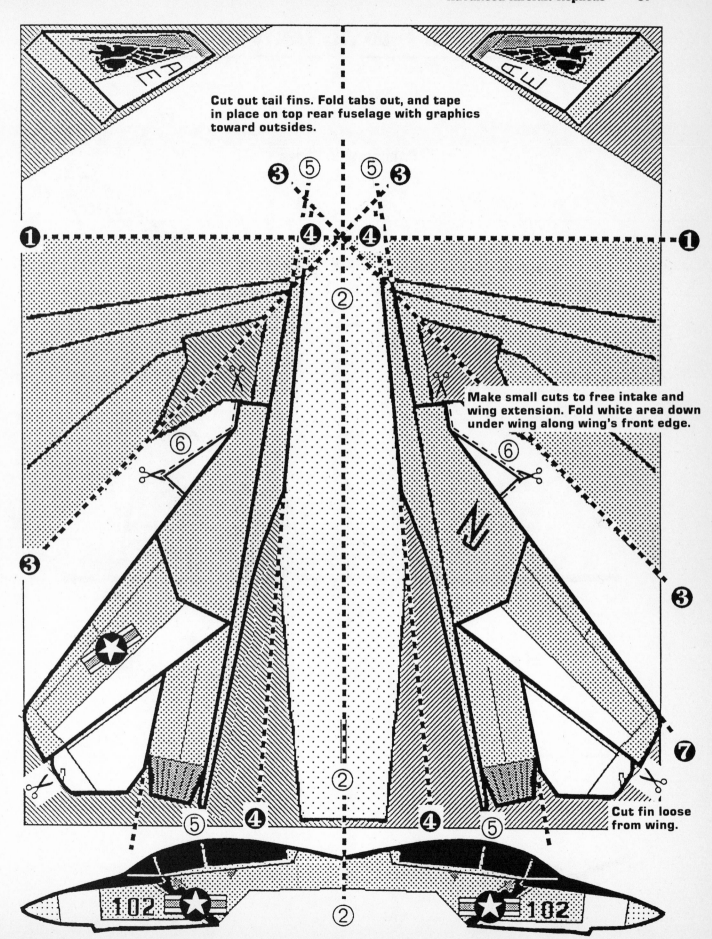

Cut out tail fins. Fold tabs out, and tape in place on top rear fuselage with graphics toward outsides.

Make small cuts to free intake and wing extension. Fold white area down under wing along wing's front edge.

Cut fin loose from wing.

General Dynamics F-16 XL Derivative

Orthographic Views

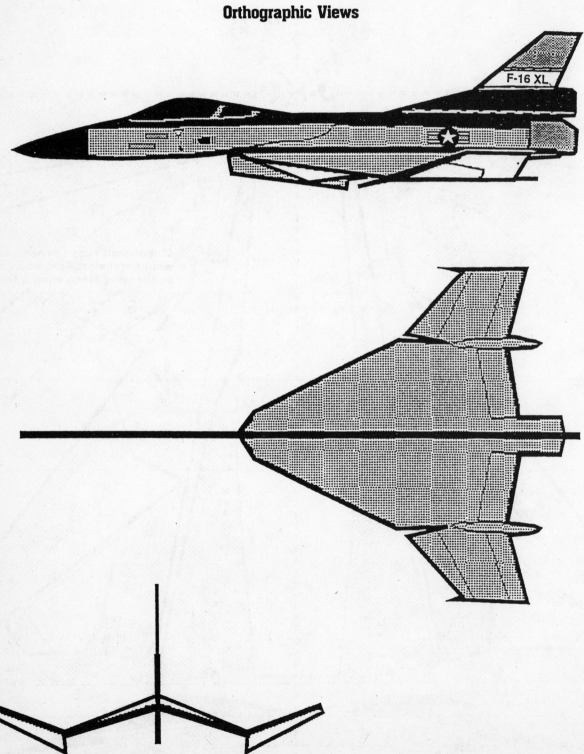

Cut, then tape into
place in rear.

Fuselage Stiffener

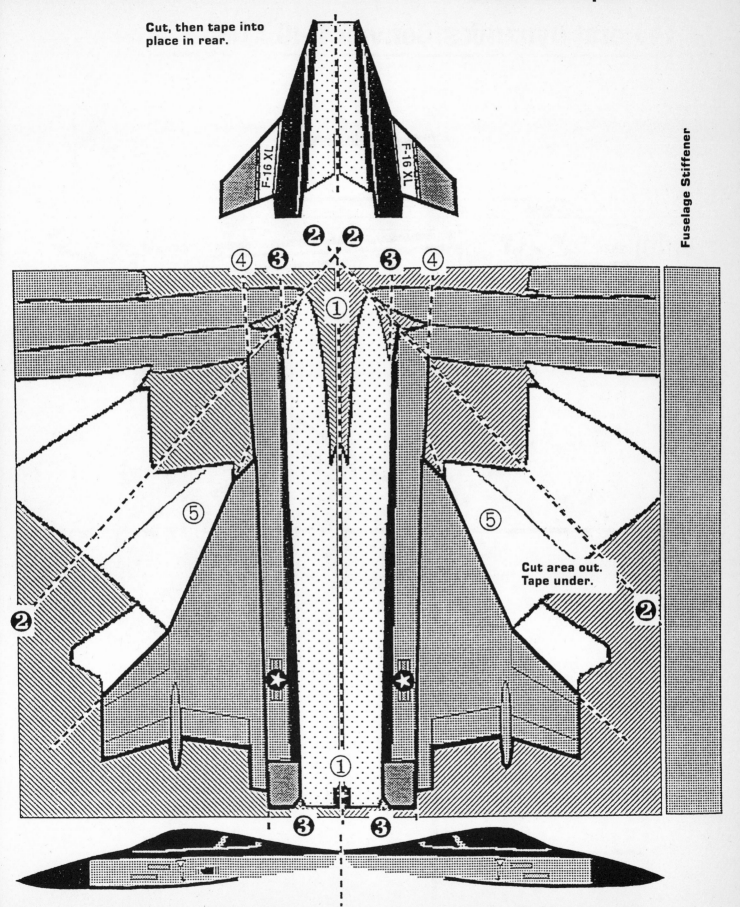

F-16 XL

F-16 XL

Cut area out.
Tape under.

Cut, fold, tape, and slide over top of fuselage, making sure the patterns and lines match.

General Dynamics/Convair F-102 Delta Dart

Orthographic Views

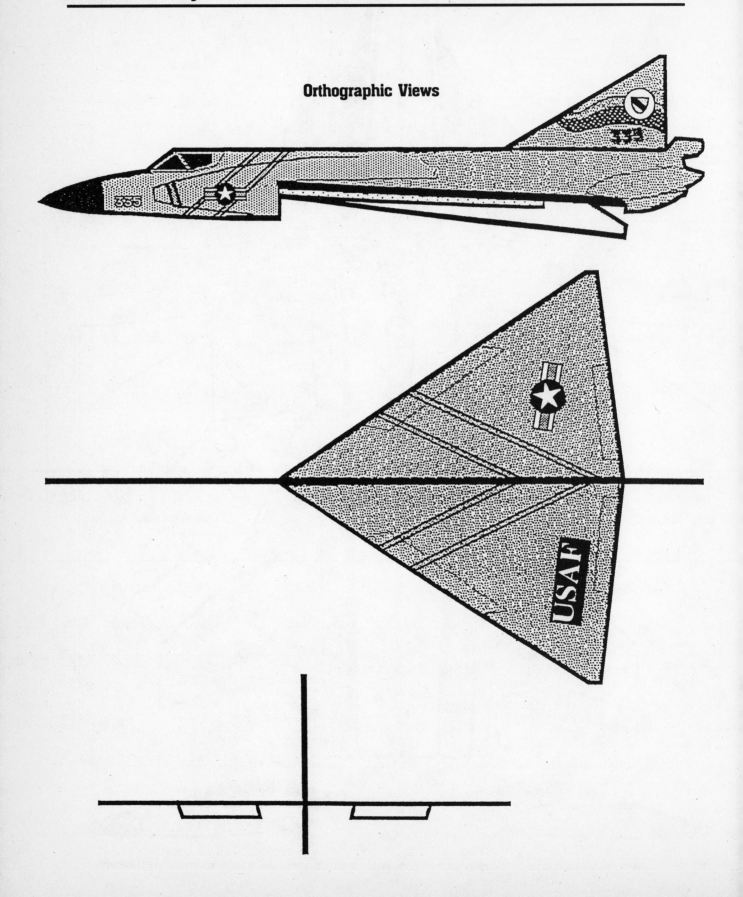

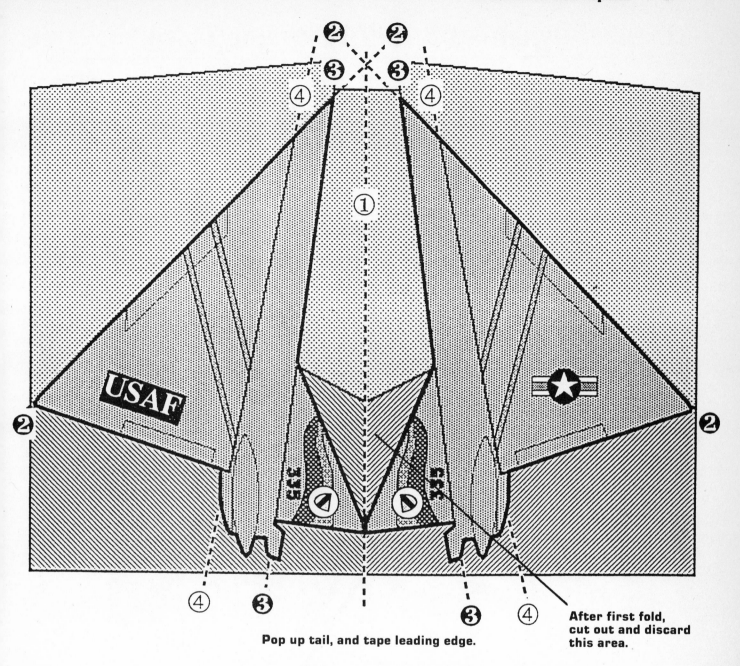

Pop up tail, and tape leading edge.

After first fold, cut out and discard this area.

USAF

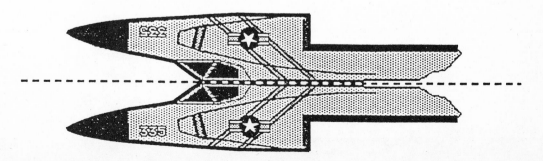

Fold in half, tape well, and insert into forward fuselage. Tape in place.

General Dynamics F-16/79 Fighting Falcon

Orthographic Views

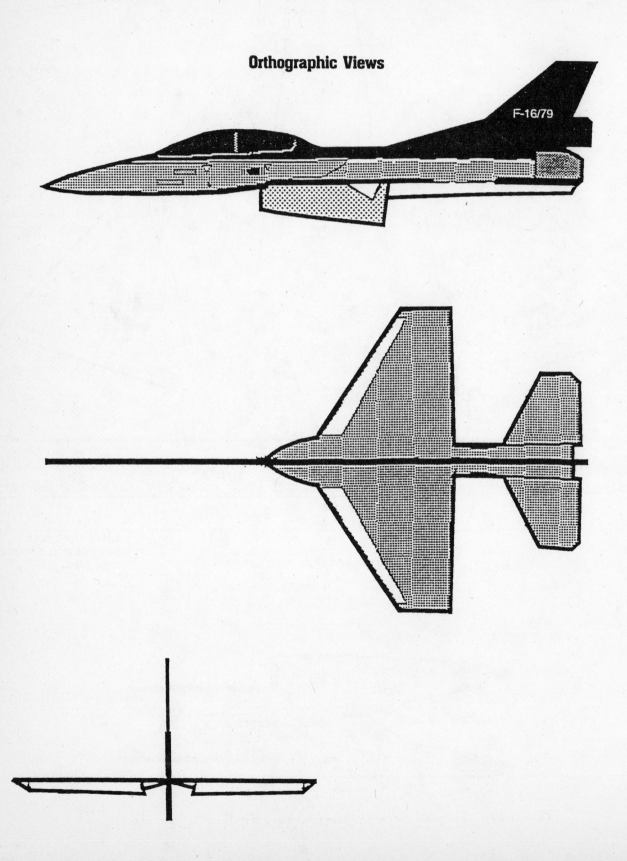

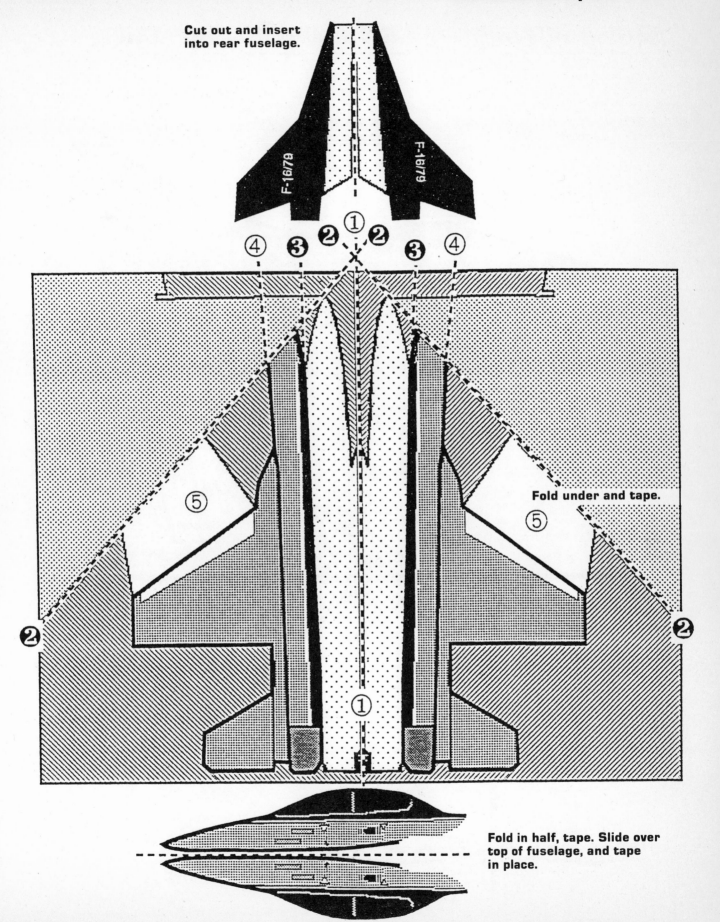

Cut out and insert into rear fuselage.

F-16/79

F-16/79

Fold under and tape.

Fold in half, tape. Slide over top of fuselage, and tape in place.

Israeli Aircraft Industries Lavi Demonstrator

Orthographic Views

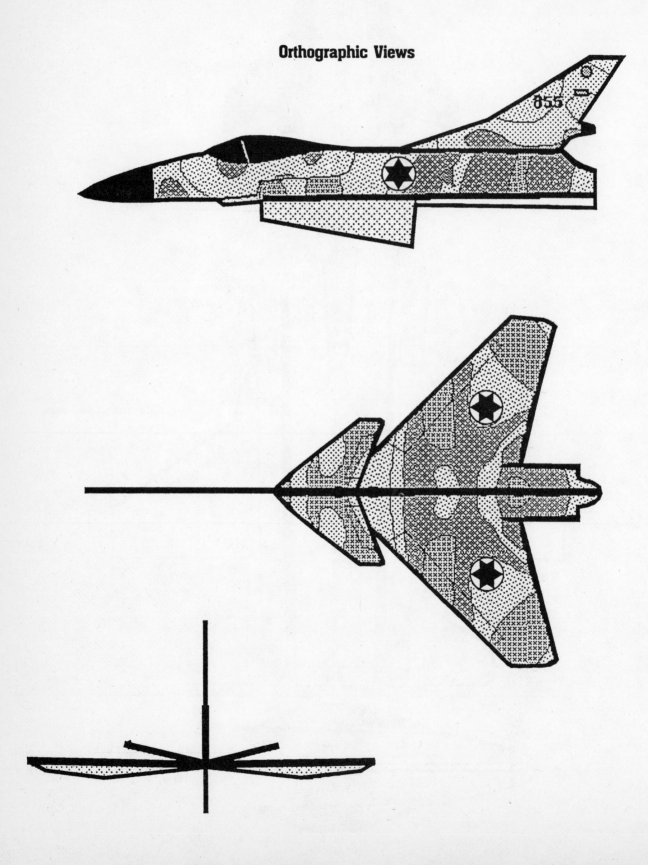

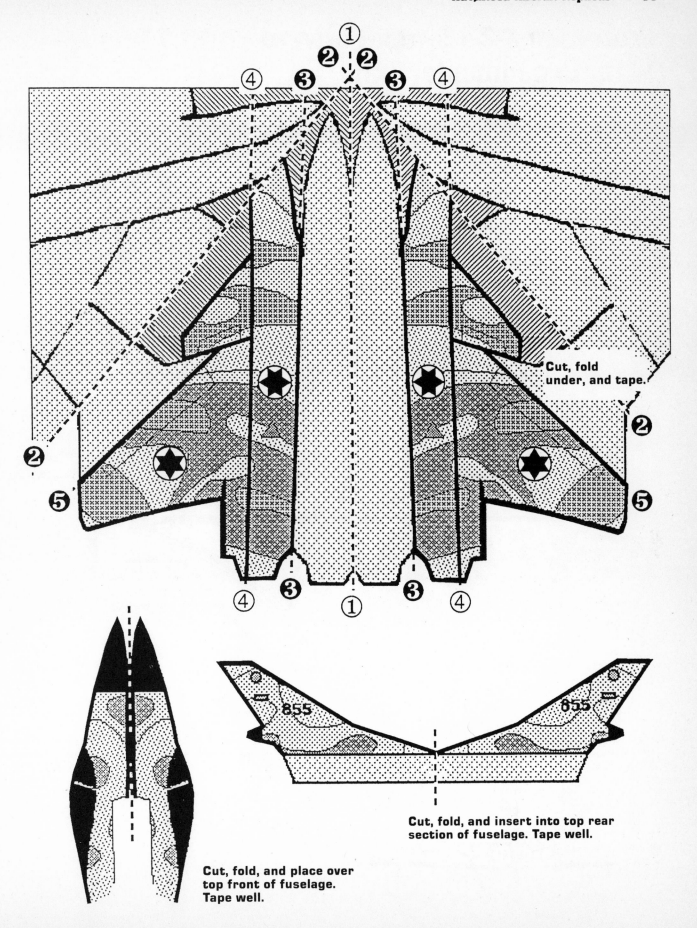

Cut, fold
under, and tape.

Cut, fold, and insert into top rear
section of fuselage. Tape well.

Cut, fold, and place over
top front of fuselage.
Tape well.

855 855

Grumman X-29 Swept-Forward Wing Experimental Craft

Orthographic Views

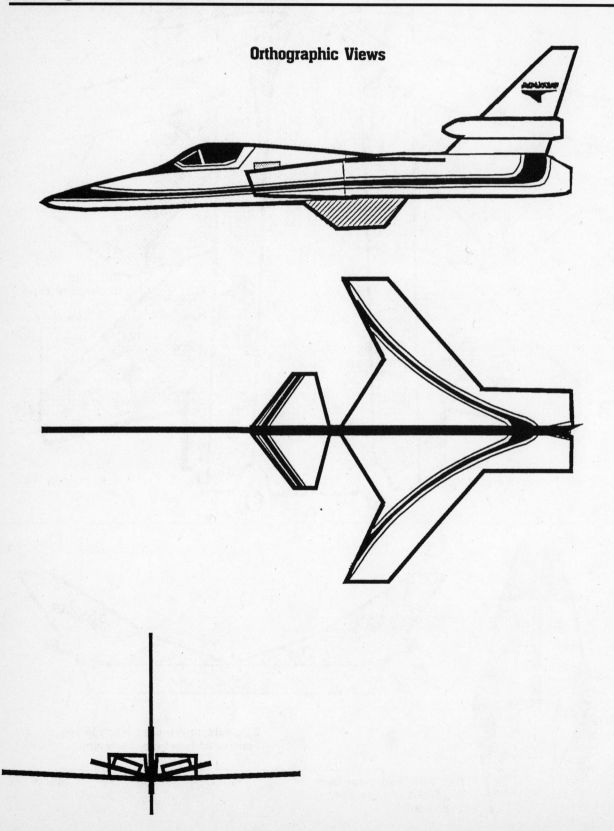

Remove large corners at the heavy diagonal lines first, to aid in construction.

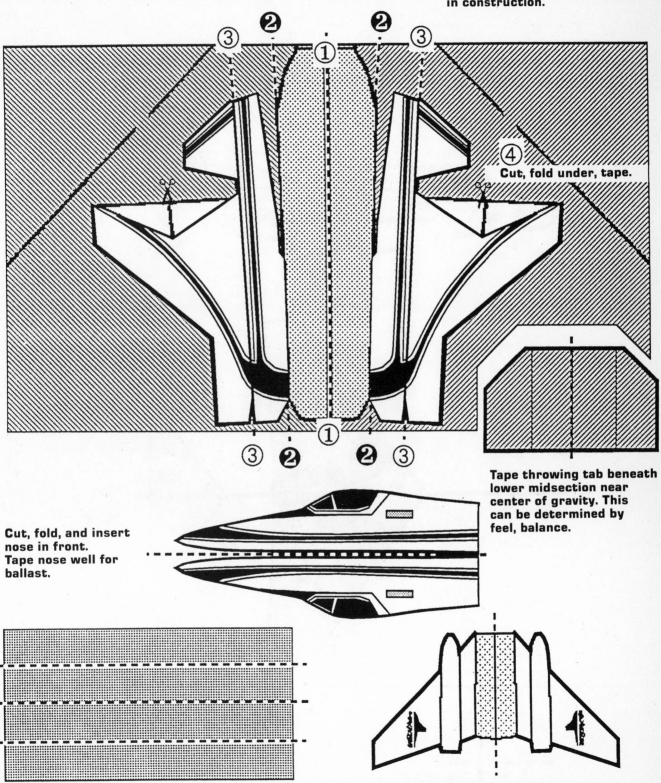

④ **Cut, fold under, tape.**

Tape throwing tab beneath lower midsection near center of gravity. This can be determined by feel, balance.

Cut, fold, and insert nose in front. Tape nose well for ballast.

Fold stiffener over twice so it is 4 layers thick. Insert fuselage stiffener in fuselage so that it spans the nose and forward fuselage section.

Cut and fold tail. Insert in upper rear fuselage.

McDonnell Douglas A-4D Skyhawk

Orthographic Views

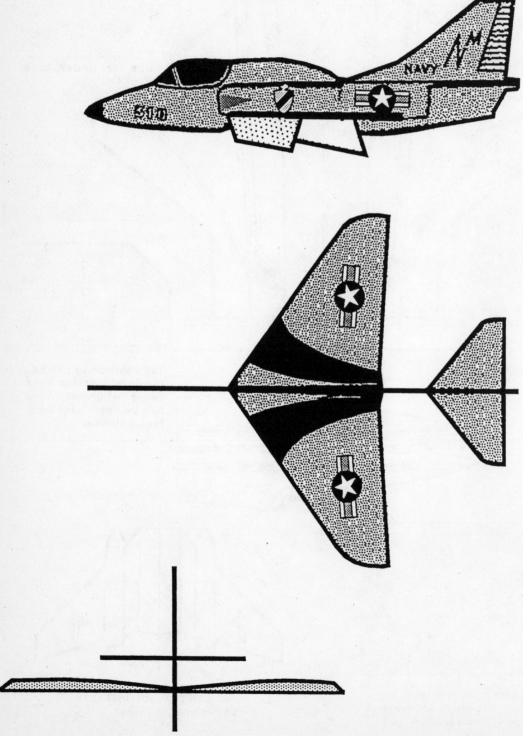

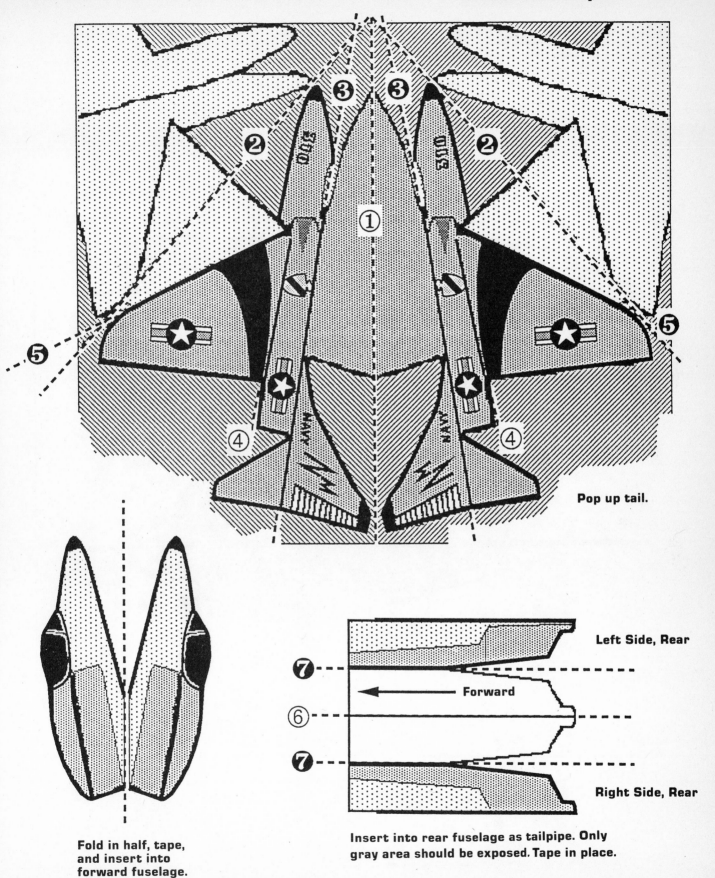

Pop up tail.

Fold in half, tape, and insert into forward fuselage. Tape in place.

Left Side, Rear

Forward

Right Side, Rear

Insert into rear fuselage as tailpipe. Only gray area should be exposed. Tape in place.

Saab J 35 Draken

Orthographic Views

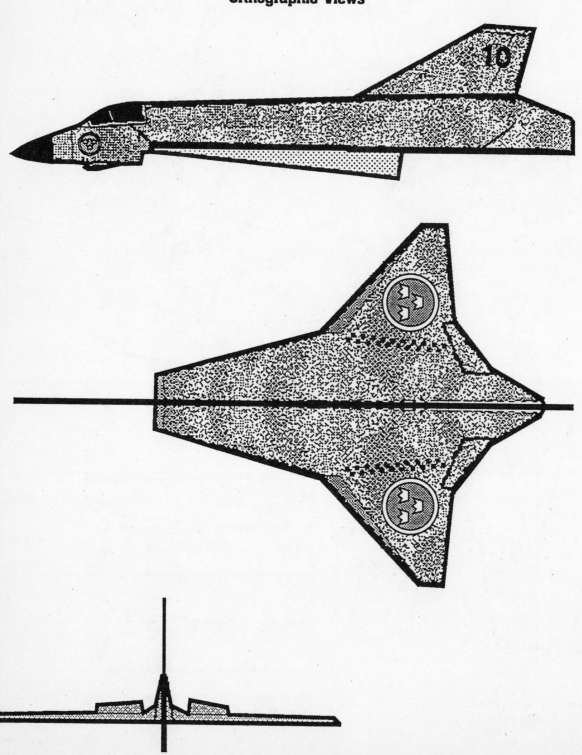

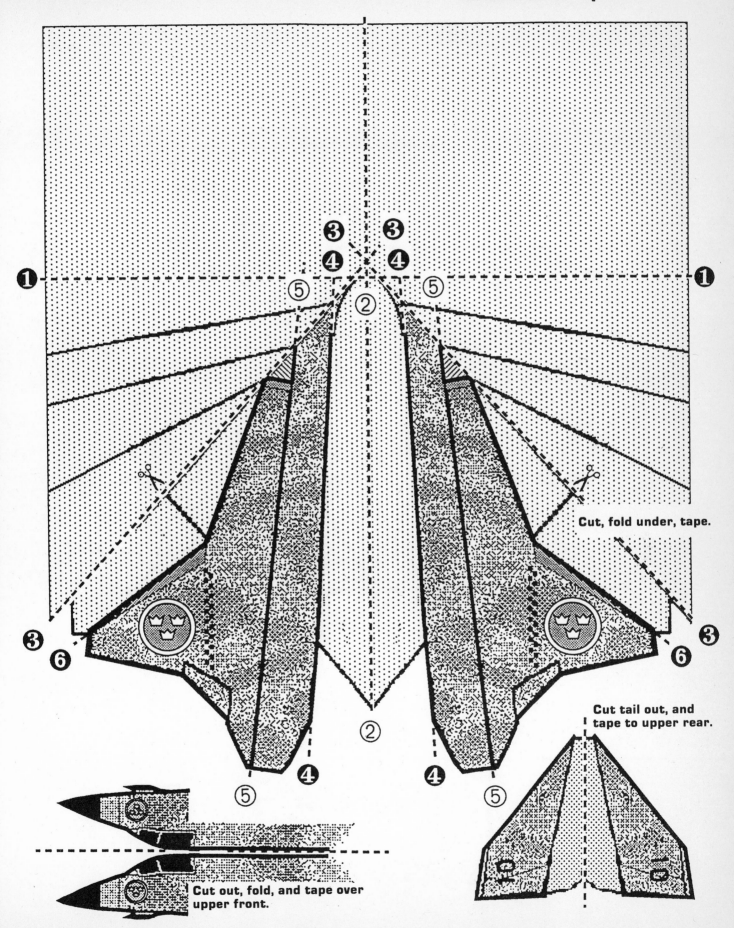

Cut, fold under, tape.

Cut tail out, and
tape to upper rear.

Cut out, fold, and tape over
upper front.

Saab JA 37 Viggen

Orthographic Views

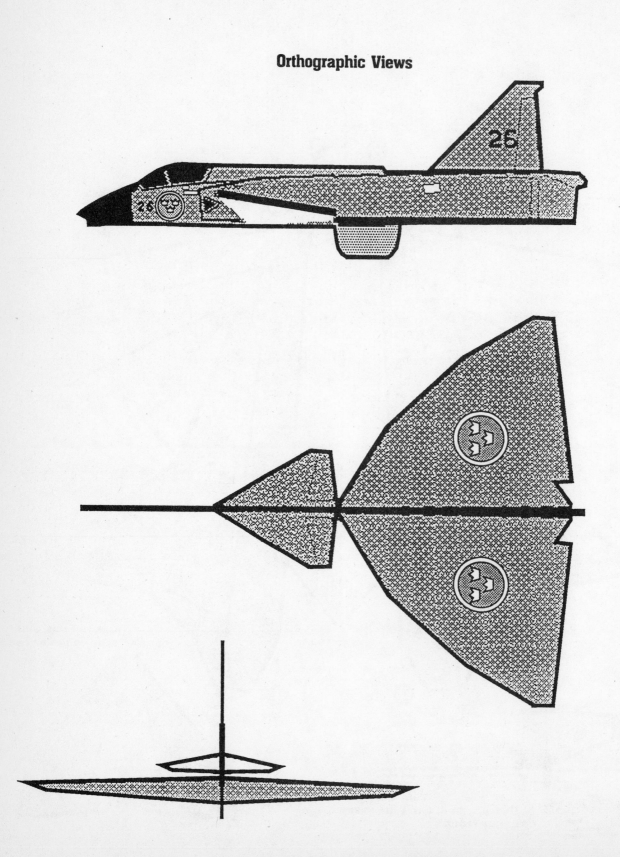

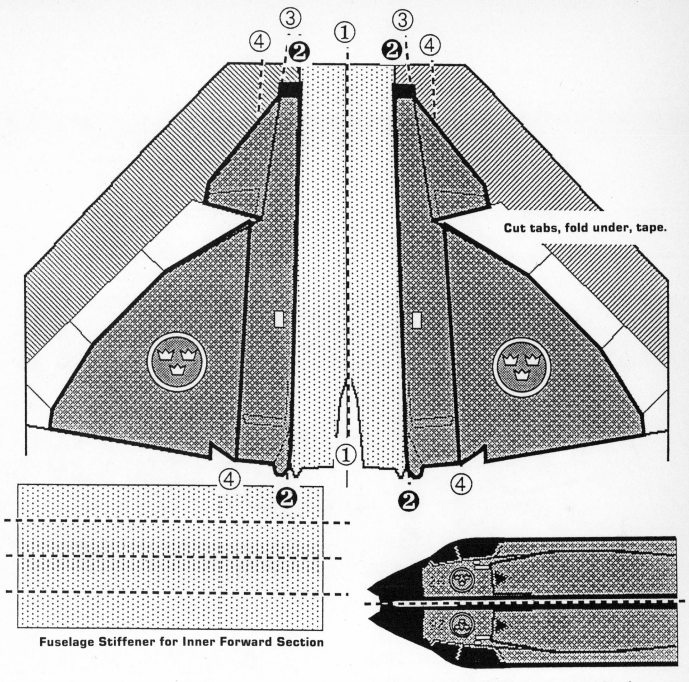

Cut tabs, fold under, tape.

Fuselage Stiffener for Inner Forward Section

Cut nose, and insert into forward fuselage.

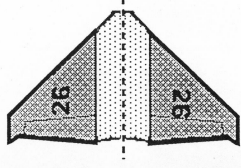

Cut tail, and insert into top rear of fuselage.

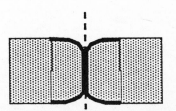

Throwing Tab—Attach to middle bottom of fuselage near center of gravity.

Alternative Design

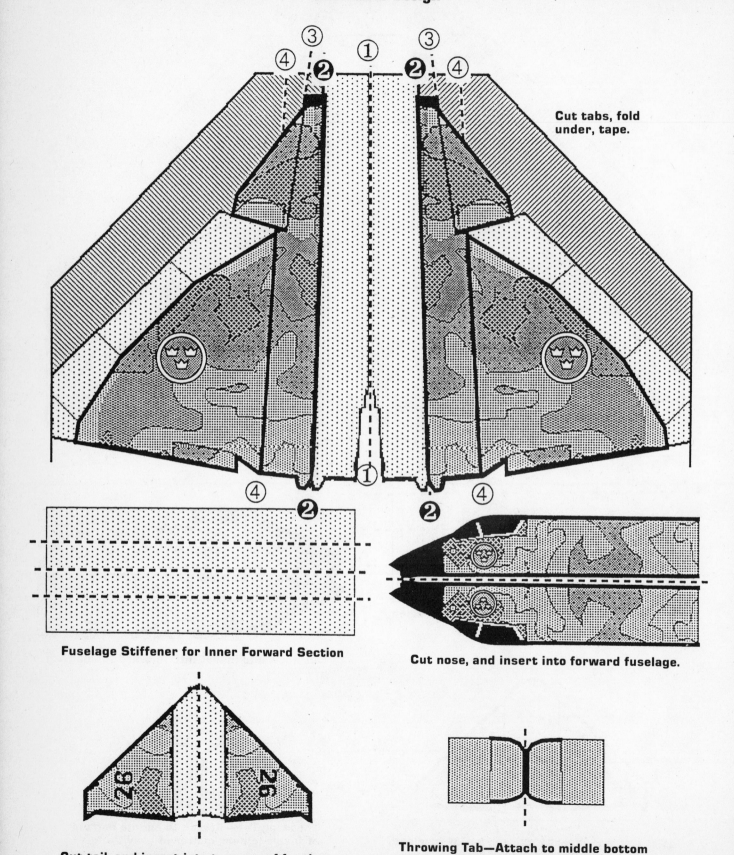

Cut tabs, fold under, tape.

Fuselage Stiffener for Inner Forward Section

Cut nose, and insert into forward fuselage.

Cut tail, and insert into top rear of fuselage.

Throwing Tab—Attach to middle bottom of fuselage near center of gravity.

Mikoyan-Guryevich MiG-21 "Fishbed-D"

Orthographic Views

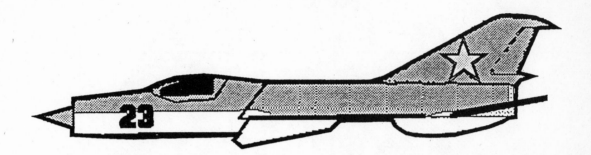

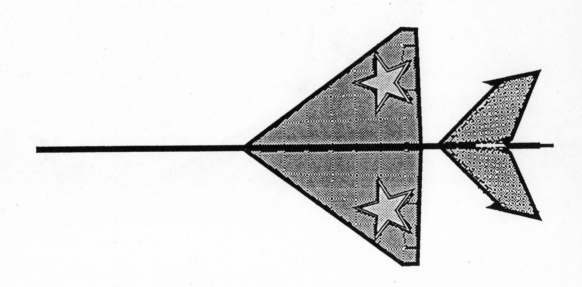

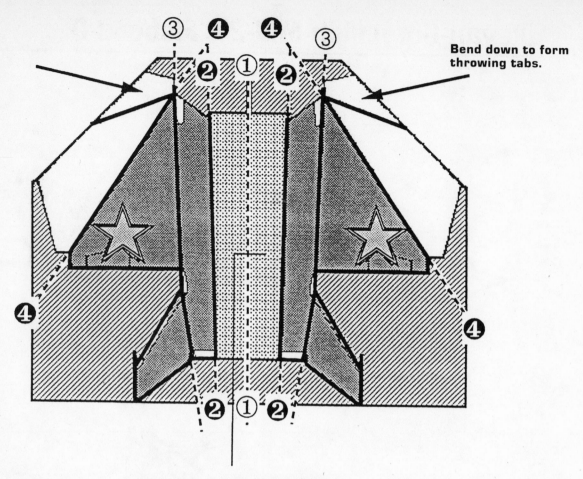

③ ④ ④ ③

② ① ②

Bend down to form throwing tabs.

④ ④

② ① ②

Slice along fold to here for tail fin.

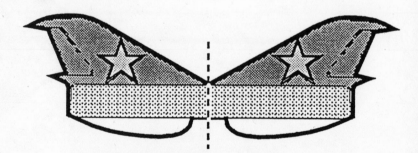

Cut, fold, and tape into rear of plane with fins protruding from both top and bottom.

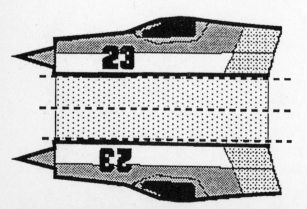

Cut, fold, and insert into front fuselage with built-in stiffener on inside.

WEAPONS

Here are some weapons to add even more realism to any of these planes.

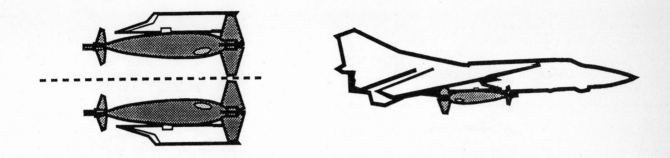

Cut, fold, and tape beneath fuselage.

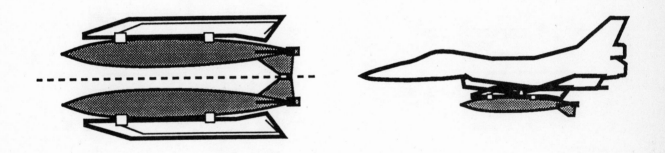

Cut, fold, and tape beneath fuselage.

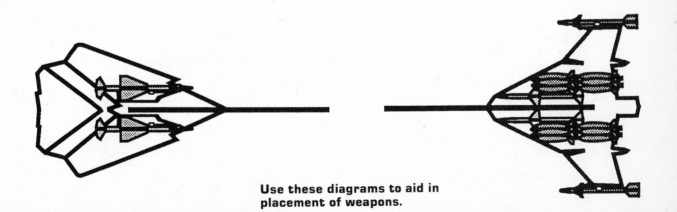

Use these diagrams to aid in placement of weapons.

Cut out missiles and bombs, and tape them to the underside of wings.

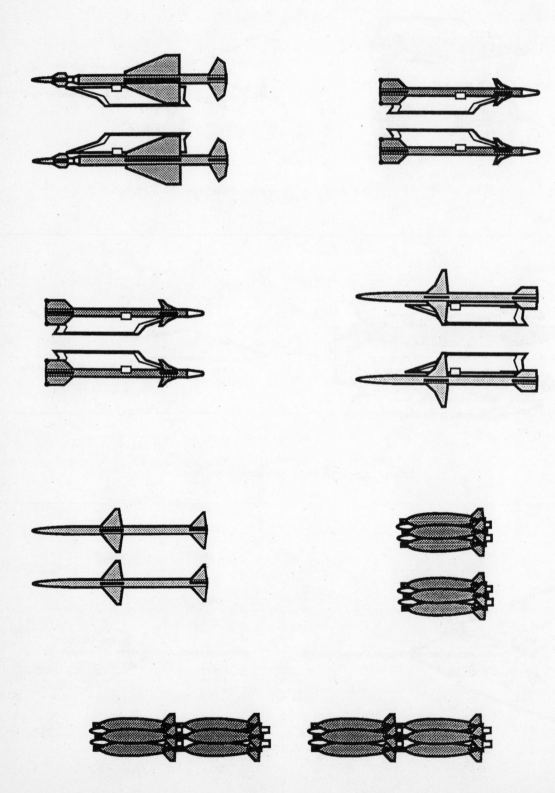

Glossary

This is a glossary of aeronautical terms used in the text. For a visual description of many of the terms, see the diagrams following the definitions.

Aerodynamics—The scientific study of how air flows around surfaces.

Aerobatics—Stunts and acrobatic maneuvers in the air.

Anhedral—The angle of wings that slightly droop down from roots to tips.

AOA—Angle of attack; the angle a surface is "tipped up" measured from a horizontal line.

Aspect ratio—The length of a wing's span; the cord of the wing.

ATF—Advanced-technology fighter.

Bernoulli effect—The force generated by the pressure difference caused by air traveling over the wing.

CAD/CAM—Computer-aided design/computer-aided manufacturing; using computers to develop 3D models and drawings.

Camber—The degree to which a surface is curved.

Canard—A horizontal control surface that looks like a small wing in front of the larger main wing.

Canopy—A typically clear area where the pilot sits.

Chines—A LERX that follows all the way along the nose of the plane to the tip; the fuselage resembles a double-edged knife laid flat.

CG—Center of gravity; the effective point where gravity acts.

Cockpit—Same as a canopy.

Cord—The length of a wing's cross section from leading to trailing edge.

Cranked arrow—A type of wing planform with two different cords, like two different-shaped triangles overlapped.

Cross section—The view seen by slicing through an object and looking at the cut section.

Dihedral—The angle of wings that rise slightly from roots to tips.

Dogtooth—A notch in the leading edge of a wing; creates better airflow and greater lift.

Drag—A force caused by air friction slowing an object's movement through the air.

Elevator—A horizontal control surface that looks like a small wing that is behind the larger main wing; also, the innermost rear flaps on the rear of the main wing.

Elevons—The outermost rear flaps on the trailing edge of the wing.

Flap—A hinged section at the front or rear of a wing; directs the flow of air.

Flaperons—Combination rear flaps/elevons/trim tabs; usually used on delta wing aircraft with no other horizontal control surface.

Flat spin—An undesireable flight path where a plane loses its forward movement and spins uncontrolled about a vertical axis. The wing stops lifting, and the plane crashes . . . very difficult to pull out of.

Fuselage—The main body of the plane.

G-force—The force an object feels if it follows a curved path like a loop. A 5-g turn feels a force five times that of the gravity.

Glide ratio—The distance a plane glides horizontally; the altitude a plane drops.

Humidity—The amount of water vapor in the air, usually expressed as a percentage. High humidity is bad for paper airplanes, as the water warps the paper.

Keel—The bottom edge of the fuselage of a paper airplane, running from the nose to the tail. It aids in stabilizing the forward flight of the plane.

Leading edge—The forward edge of the wing.

LERX—Leading edge root extension; a device used to smooth the flow of air before it actually hits the main wing.

Lift—A force pulling up on an object against gravity.

Ordnance—Weapons, bombs, missles.

Pitch—Pivoting the plane about an axis running horizontally through the main wing.

Planform (planview)—The top view of an object.

Roll—Pivoting the plane about an axis running the length of the fuselage.

RSW—Rear-swept wing.

Rudder—The rear-located vertical stabilizing surface; a plane can have more than one.

SFW—Swept-forward wing.

Slab tail surfaces—Horizontal tail control surfaces that move as one unit with no trim tabs.

Slat—A combination flap-slot.

Slot—A long hole along the leading edge of a wing to aid lift at high AOAs.

Stalling—The point where a wing fails to create lift due to an extreme angle of attack.

Stealth—Type of features that allow a plane to move undetected by normal means.

Supercritical—A stretched wing cross section with a flat top suitable for high-speed flight.

Symmetrical—Having the same shape on either side of a central dividing line.

Thrust—A force propelling an object in a forward motion.

Trailing edge—The rear edge of a wing.

Trim tab—A small flap for fine-tuning a plane's flights.

Turbulence—"Rough" air that leaves a surface in a disturbed path.

Vortex flaps—Sharp, drooped leading edge flaps that speed up the airflow over a wing much as a dogtooth does.

Wing—The main horizontal lifting surface on a plane.

Weight—A force from gravity caused by an object's mass pulling it toward the ground.

Wing fence—A device to straighten the airflow over a wing.

Winglets—Bending the last bit of the wing tip up or down at right angles to smooth airflow around the tip.

Yaw—Pivoting the plane about a vertical axis.

POSSIBLE CONTROL SURFACES AND
THE AXES OF MOTION THEY INFLUENCE

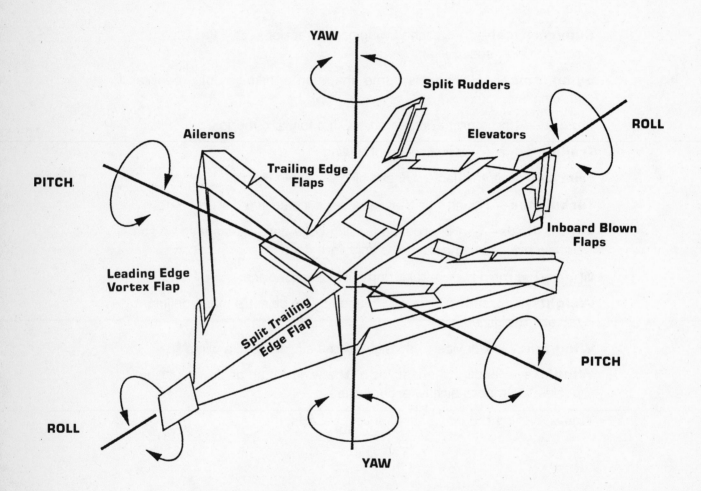

**CONTROL SURFACE SETTINGS, TO EXECUTE A SMOOTH
LEFT BANKING TURN ON THE INTERCEPTOR AIRCRAFT**

REAR VIEW

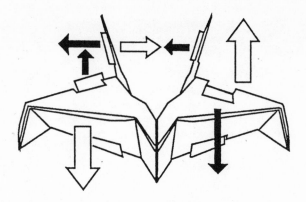

Light arrows show
reaction motion of
aircraft surface.

Dark arrows indicate
direction of deflected
airstream.

**CONTROL SURFACE SETTINGS ON
ADVANCED FIGHTER TO EXECUTE A SLIDING TURN WITHOUT
BANKING (I.E., "BAT TURN").**

FRONT VIEW

Rudders are
fully deflected.

Trim tabs are only
slightly deflected.